The World of Carbon

The World of Carbon

ISAAC ASIMOV

NEW, REVISED EDITION

COLLIER BOOKS
A Division of Macmillan Publishing Co., Inc.
NEW YORK
COLLIER MACMILLAN PUBLISHERS
LONDON

To All Those Who Taught Me

Acknowledgments

To: Mrs. Joan Smith McLellan, who prepared the formulas
To: Robert Bernard Aronson, who reviewed the manuscript

Contents

Introduction—The Two Halves of Chemistry

Animal, Vegetable, or Mineral

CHEMISTS DIVIDE all substances into two classes. In one class are such things as olive oil, sugar, starch, glue, gelatin, silk, rubber, paper, and penicillin. These are examples of *organic* substances. In the other class are such things as air, water, sand, clay, salt, gold, silver, iron, brass, glass, and concrete. These are examples of *inorganic* substances.

Why these two groups? Let's see.

This division was first invented in 1807 by Jöns Jakob Berzelius, a Swedish chemist. At that time, chemistry was a very young science. Very little was known about the real makeup of most substances.

Even then, though, one fact seemed clear. Some substances were found in the soil or in the oceans and air about us. They had been there, apparently, since the earth began—sand or water, for instance.

Other things, however, existed only because they had been manufactured by some living creature—sugar, for instance. There are no sugar mines. You can't get sugar by digging in the ground. You must depend on some form of life. You must cultivate the sugar cane, or sugar beet, or sugar maple, and extract the sugar from the juices of the plant.

Berzelius, therefore, called substances that could be obtained from living organisms, organic. Everything else was inorganic. The first class was the product of life; the second was not. If you have ever played the game, "animal, vegetable, or mineral," you would classify organic substances as animal or vegetable. Inorganic substances would be mineral.

At the time, this seemed to be a good way of dividing up substances. Organic materials seemed different from inorganic materials in a number of ways. For example, organic materials are much more fragile and easily damaged than inorganic materials.

Water (which is inorganic) can be boiled and the resulting steam heated to a thousand degrees without damage. When the steam is cooled down, water is formed again. If olive oil (which is organic) is heated, it will smoke and burn. After that, it will no longer be olive oil.

You can heat salt (which is inorganic) till it melts and becomes red-hot. Cool it again and it is still salt. If sugar (which is organic) is heated, it will give off vapors, then char and turn black. Cooling will not restore its original nature.

There was another point of difference that struck the early chemists even more sharply. Organic substances can be treated with heat or by other methods and converted into inorganic substances. There seemed no way, however, of starting with an inorganic substance and converting it to an organic substance.

Organic substances seemed to be the product of living tissue alone. The early chemists thought that perhaps some mysterious "vital force" was necessary to produce them. They thought the "vital force" could be found only in living tissue and they despaired of being able to copy nature in the laboratory.

Then, in 1827, came the big break. It involved an organic substance called *urea*. This is a white solid which is one of the waste-products of the body. An adult human being produces up to an ounce of it each day and gets rid of it in dissolved form in the urine.

Until 1827, chemists were convinced that only the living body could form urea. In that year, however, Friedrich Wöhler, a German chemist, found out differently, to his own amazement. He found that if he heated an inorganic substance called *ammonium cyanate*, it changed into urea. Something inorganic had changed into something organic in the test-tube. Wöhler ran the experiment over and over again before he dared announce the results. When he did, in 1828, the report stunned the chemical world.

But there was no mistake about it. Before very long, chemists were making a number of organic substances in the laboratory, starting with inorganic materials. The original reason for dividing chemical substances into two classes no longer existed.

Carbon and No Carbon

Still the classification was not abandoned. Other important differences between the two groups showed up.

Both organic and inorganic substances are made up of atoms[1] of different kinds. It turned out that the substances which Berzelius called organic were made up of molecules that always contained at least one *carbon atom*. Substances which Berzelius called inorganic sometimes contained carbon atoms in their molecules, but usually did not.

It turned out to be convenient, therefore, to call any substance with carbon atoms in its molecule organic, whether it occurred in living tissue or not. Any substance without carbon atoms in its molecule was inorganic. This is not exactly the same division as the one invented by Berzelius, of course.

It may seem to you that these two halves of chemistry must be very unequal in size. Organic chemistry concentrates on a single type of atom and leaves all the rest to the inorganic chemists.

Yes, the division is unequal, but not in the way you might think. It is the organic compounds that are more numerous. There are many more compounds that contain carbon than compounds that do not. At least 1,700,000 carbon-containing compounds are already known and more are being discovered in nature or formed in the laboratory every day. There seems to be no end to the process. As compared with this, the total number of inorganic compounds—of all the elements other than carbon—come to only about 500,000.

---

[1] Some definitions at this point might be helpful. An *atom* is the smallest particle of normal matter. In most substances, atoms don't exist in isolated form but exist in groups that hang together and behave as a unit. These groups are called *molecules*. A *pure substance* is any material made up of only one kind of molecule. An *element* is a pure substance whose molecules are made up of only one kind of atom. A *compound* is a pure substance whose molecules are made up of more than one kind of atom.

Why is this? Well, when atoms (other than carbon) are hooked together to form molecules, the best results are obtained when only a few atoms are involved. A molecule made up of only two or three atoms is often quite strong and the atoms hold together firmly. As more atoms are added, however, the molecule becomes rickety and it is more and more likely to fall apart. An inorganic molecule containing more than a dozen atoms is, for that reason, quite rare.

Molecules containing carbon atoms are an exception to this general rule. Carbon atoms can join one another to form long chains or numerous rings and then join with other kinds of atoms as well. Very large molecules may be formed in this way without becoming too rickety to exist. It is not at all unusual for an organic molecule to contain a million atoms.

Imagine two children, each with a set of blocks. One has a set containing some ninety different kinds that he can put together to build, let's say, a house. However, he may use only ten or twelve blocks at a time. The second child has a set containing only four or five kinds of blocks, but he may use any number he chooses to build a house—a million blocks, if he wishes.

Obviously, the second child could build a greater number of different houses.

It is exactly for that reason that there are many more organic compounds than there are inorganic compounds.

In this book, I will discuss some of the various types of organic compounds that exist. You will see their importance and be shown how an increased knowledge of their structure has led to a better life for all of us.

Diagrams for Molecules

Before I can do that I must discuss one problem that can't be avoided if we are to deal with large molecules. By the middle 1800s, organic compounds had piled up by the hundreds and even thousands. How could one chemist describe the various compounds so that another chemist would see what the atomic structure must be?

For inorganic compounds, chemists can get by with *formulas*. These are made up of symbols for the various kinds of atoms. Often the symbol is simply the initial letter of the name of the atom. Thus, the symbol for the carbon atom is C. The symbol for the hydrogen atom is H; for the oxygen atom, O; for the nitrogen atom, N. What could be simpler?

Now it is only necessary to list the number of each kind of atom in the molecule of a particular compound. That will be its formula. For instance, the water molecule contains two hydrogen atoms and one oxygen atom. The formula for water could therefore be written H_2O_1. Actually, though, when only a single atom of a particular kind is present, the numeral "1" is left out. The formula for water is therefore written as H_2O. Notice that the numbers are small and written a little below the line. Such numbers are called *subscripts* (from Latin words meaning "written under").

This trick won't do where organic compounds are concerned. There are so many of them that it frequently happens that two or more different compounds have molecules made up of the same number and kinds of atoms. For instance, two organic compounds—one called *ethyl alcohol* and one *dimethyl ether*—have molecules made up of two carbon atoms, six hydrogen atoms, and one oxygen atom. The formula for both would be C_2H_6O. Yet the two substances are different in behavior and are two different compounds. Their molecules are made up of the same atoms, but these atoms are arranged differently in each.

In these days of "do-it-yourself," some of us may have experienced a similar problem. We sometimes buy some ordinary object in a department store—perhaps some porch furniture. When we open the carton, we may find a number of metal rods and sheets, together with nuts and bolts of various kinds, and washers of various shapes.

Well, all the parts are there, but unless we are skilled mechanics, that doesn't help us. There's the problem of putting the parts together in the correct arrangement. The same parts put together incorrectly will not give us what we want.

To help us, the manufacturers usually enclose a set of instructions, together with a diagram showing us the different parts and the way they fit together. Without the diagram, most of us would be helpless.

There you are. In the case of complicated organic

molecules, listing the number of atoms present is not enough. We need a diagram to show how the different atoms fit together.

In 1859, Friedrich August Kekulé, a German chemist, invented the *structural formula*. That is, he wrote down the symbol for each atom present in a particular molecule. Then he connected the various symbols with short lines according to the way in which the atoms were arranged within the molecule.

Occasionally, in this book, I will use such formulas. They are nothing to be afraid of. I will explain each one as I come to it and you will see that they are not at all difficult to understand. In fact, if you were to try to learn about organic chemicals without using formulas, you would have to quit very soon. It would be like trying to put together a complicated machine that you have never seen before without any diagrams to help you.

Try to keep that in mind and you will have no trouble.

The World of Carbon

Chapter 1

Chains, Long and Short

The Simplest Organic Compound

IT IS A good idea, I think, to start with something simple. There are compounds with molecules made up of only carbon atoms and hydrogen atoms. These are the two kinds of atoms that occur most frequently in organic compounds, so they're the logical ones to start with. Compounds made up of carbon atoms and hydrogen atoms only are called *hydrocarbons*.

The simplest hydrocarbon, naturally, is one with a molecule containing only a single carbon atom. A carbon atom is capable of hooking on to four other atoms. A hydrogen atom is capable of hooking on to only one other atom.

This means that one carbon atom can be connected with four hydrogen atoms. So we write a C for carbon, surround it by four H's for hydrogen, and connect each H to the C by little lines called *bonds*. thus:

Figure 1— Methane

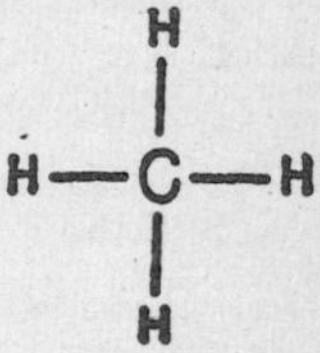

This compound is *methane,* and it is the simplest organic molecule of all.

Methane is a gas, colorless and odorless, like the air about us. Like all gases, it can be turned into a liquid if it is made cold enough. However, the temperature required to liquefy methane can be reached only in specially equipped laboratories. Even the coldest winters in Antarctica wouldn't be nearly cold enough.

An important characteristic (or *property*) of methane is that it will burn. That is, when methane is heated in air, the carbon and hydrogen atoms in the molecule break away from one another and combine with the oxygen present in the air. Each atom of carbon combines with two atoms of oxygen to form a molecule of carbon dioxide. Each pair of hydrogen atoms combines with one oxygen atom to form a molecule of water. In the process, light is produced and heat is given off.

This is a very useful property. Methane can be led through pipes into houses (together with other inflammable gases, such as hydrogen or carbon monoxide). By setting fire to this gas in ranges and furnaces we can cook food and heat houses.

In general, almost any organic compound, if heated enough, will burn. The majority of inorganic compounds, on the other hand, will not burn.

Methane sometimes forms when once-living matter decays and decomposes under water or underground. In marshy areas, the decay of tree stumps and of other vegetable matter under water produces bubbles of gas that consist mostly of methane. For this reason, methane is sometimes called *marsh gas*.

Methane also occurs in tiny pockets in coal beds. Coal (which is made up mostly of carbon atoms) is formed from once-living matter that has slowly decayed underground. Small quantities of methane are also formed and are trapped in the coal. As the miners break up the seams of coal, enough methane can seep into the air of the mines to become dangerous. If enough methane mixes with the air, the smallest spark may cause its molecules to combine with the oxygen of the air so suddenly that an explosion results. Miners call methane, *fire-damp* ("damp" being an old-fashioned word for "gas") and must guard against its presence.

Building up the Chains

Suppose, now, we place a bond between two carbon atoms. Each carbon atom has thus used up one bond but still has the ability to form bonds with three other atoms. If all those other atoms are hydrogen, this is what the molecule will look like:

Figure 2—Ethane

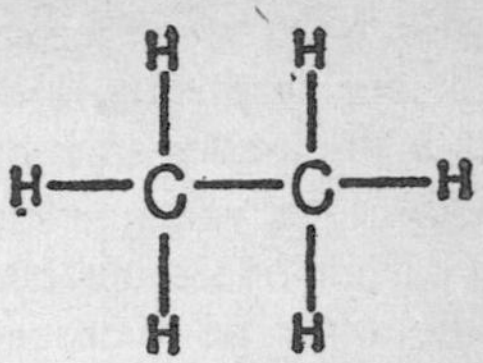

Molecules like these make up the compound *ethane*. Ethane is a gas with properties similar to those of methane.

You can build the chain further. Three carbons bonded together and surrounded by hydrogens make up the molecule of *propane*. Four carbons and the necessary hydrogen make up *butane*.

Propane and butane are also gases. However, as the molecules get larger, it becomes easier to liquefy them. (This is a general rule among organic compounds.) An Antarctic winter is sufficient to liquefy propane and even a New York winter will liquefy butane.

Propane and butane will burn like methane. Quantities of these more complicated gases can be forced, under pressure into metal cylinders. These cylinders can be attached to ranges and the gas allowed to feed slowly into the jets and burn. This can be very handy in isolated regions where cooking-gas is not supplied through pipes by large gas companies.

We needn't stop at butane. Five carbons can be bound together; or six, or seven, or eight, or, for that matter, even seventy or ninety. Chemists do not try to think up different names for each new string of carbon atoms. Once they get to hydrocarbons with more than four carbons in the molecule, they generally use numbers. There is one catch, alas. They use Greek numbers.

For instance, a hydrocarbon with five carbons is called *pentane*. The prefix, "pent," comes from a Greek word meaning "five." In the same way, the next three hydrocarbons are called *hexane, heptane,* and *octane.* "Hex," "hept" and "oct" are from Greek words meaning "six," "seven," and "eight."

The word "octane" may ring a bell with you. Perhaps you have heard of the word in connection with *gasoline*. If you have, it is not surprising. Gasoline is a mixture of various hydrocarbon molecules such as heptane and octane.

But gasoline, as you know, is a liquid. Remember, that as the hydrocarbon molecule becomes larger, it also becomes easier to liquefy. The hydrocarbon molecules in gasoline are so large they need not be cooled at all to form a liquid. They are liquid at ordinary temperatures.

The mixture of liquid hydrocarbons in gasoline is *volatile*. That is, the liquids tend to vaporize easily. It is those vapors you smell when a gas-station attendant fills an automobile's gas-tank. (Incidentally, gasoline is often spoken of as simply "gas." This is not a good nickname, because the word "gas" means any vapor.) Gasoline vapors, if mixed with air, will explode just as methane will. It is for that reason that gasoline is a fire hazard.

Inside the automobile motor, the explosion of gasoline vapors is made useful. The vapors are mixed with air in the carburetor and the mixture is fed into the cylinders. There it is exploded by means of an electric spark from the spark-plug. These explosions drive the pistons which in turn supply the force that moves the car.

Cigarette-lighter fluid, by the way, consists of a mixture of liquid hydrocarbons very similar to that in gasoline.

Branches in the Chain

Some kinds of gasolines are more expensive than others. We must return to our structural formulas to understand why.

When you imagine a hydrocarbon with seven or eight carbon atoms, it is a pretty safe bet that you think of the carbon atoms strung out in a straight line. It doesn't have to be that way, though. You can put the carbon atoms together in just about any way you wish.

Take butane, the four-carbon hydrocarbon, as an example. It can be put together in two different ways, as follows:

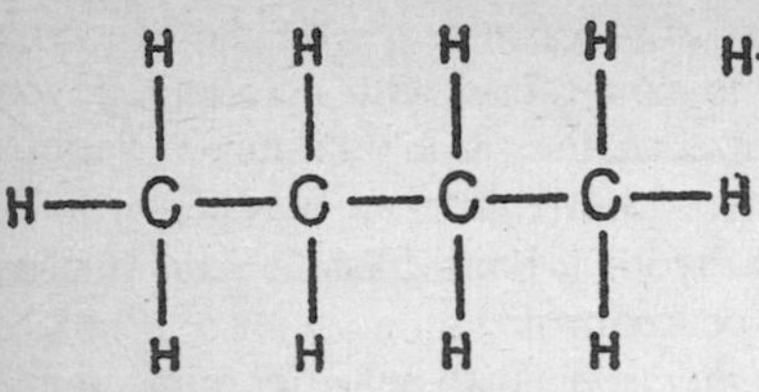

Figure 3—Normal Butane 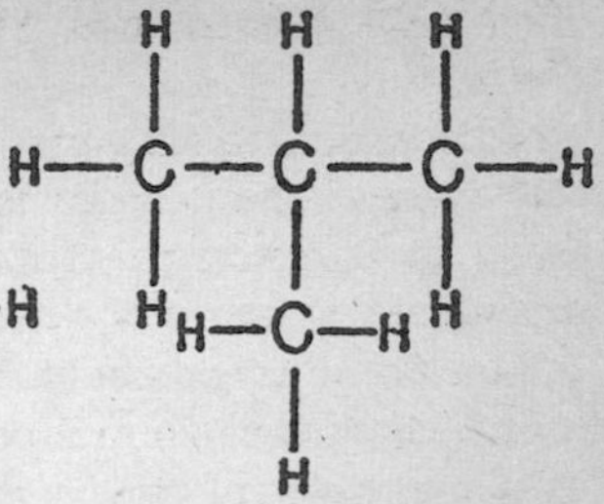   *Figure 4—Isobutane*

If you count the atoms in each molecule, you'll find that each has four carbon atoms and ten hydrogen atoms. The two molecules have somewhat different properties despite this, because the atoms are arranged differently. Molecules which have the same number and kinds of atoms, but have them arranged differently, are called *isomers*. A molecule with four carbon atoms in a straight line (a straight-chain compound) is called *normal butane*. One with four carbons not in a straight line (a branched-chain compound) is called *isobutane*.[1]

For a four-carbon compound, only two arrangements of the carbon atoms are possible. With more carbon atoms in the molecule, the number of possible arrangements increases rapidly. After all, you can branch the chain at different points; you can have more than one branch; you can have branches of different lengths; you can have branches on the branches.

Octane, with eight carbon atoms, shows eighteen possible arrangements of the carbon atoms of the chain. That means that eighteen different octanes, each with eight carbon atoms and eighteen hydrogen atoms in the molecule can exist. Each one of the eighteen octanes behaves a little differently.

[1] Isomers often differ only slightly in their properties. Isobutane is a little harder to liquefy than normal butane, for instance, but not much. You may wonder if small differences are worth worrying about. The answer is, yes—and sometimes the differences aren't so small. There are many compounds that are vital to the body's workings, but become useless to it if the arrangement of atoms in the molecule is ever so slightly altered.

Each has to be studied separately if it is to be understood thoroughly.[2]

The various hydrocarbons in gasoline all burn if heated. All will explode if their vapor is mixed with air and a spark is set to the mixture. However, they don't all burn in quite the same way. Here is where isomer differences become quite important. Straight-chain hydrocarbons burn a little faster than branched-chain hydrocarbons do.

If the vapor of *normal heptane* (with seven carbon atoms in a straight line) is set burning within an automobile cylinder, explosion is too rapid. There is the sound of a "pop" inside the cylinder. The piston is jarred and its in-and-out rhythm is upset. This is called *engine knock*. It represents wasted power and possible engine damage.

Other hydrocarbons behave better. In particular, there is an isomer of octane with three small branches in its carbon chain, that behaves very well. This isomer is called *isooctane*. When the spark sets off a mixture of isooctane and air, the explosion takes place more slowly than in the case of heptane. First the molecules of isooctane near the spark explode, then those a little further away, then those still further away and so on. There is no "pop" and no jar. The piston is allowed a full, rhythmic stroke and power is delivered efficiently.

A particular type of gasoline is given an *octane rating*, depending on the amount of engine knock that is produced. Normal heptane by itself would have a zero-octane rating. Isooctane would have a hundred-octane rating. By comparing the way in which a particular gasoline burns with the way different mixtures of normal heptane and isooctane burn, the octane rating of that gasoline can be determined. The higher the octane rating of a gasoline, the more efficient it is, and the more expensive.

Chemists have found ways of decreasing knock by adding

---

[2] It has been calculated that a forty-carbon compound would show more than sixty trillion possible arrangements. Each of them would be a different compound. Naturally, chemists don't bother about all those different isomers or try to locate each one. There are more important problems to tackle. Still, it shows why there are so many different organic compounds.

certain anti-knock compounds to gasoline. The best known of these is a compound which contains a lead atom in its molecule and which is known as *tetraethyl lead*. Gasoline needs less than a tenth of a percent of it for good results. Such gasoline is known as ethyl gasoline or leaded gasoline. Leaded gasoline is deliberately colored because its lead content makes is more poisonous than ordinary gasoline, and it must be handled more carefully.

The octane rating of gasoline for sale to the public has improved continuously. In 1937, most makes of gasoline had octane ratings of 73 to 80. Now, premium gasolines have octane ratings of 95 or more. In fact, special gasolines with octane ratings higher than 100 have been prepared, particularly for use in aircraft. These "super-premium" gasolines are now in use for the specially powerful engines in late model cars.

Where Hydrocarbons Come From

There is a kind of oil that exists underground in some regions of the earth. Until about a hundred years ago, it was nothing more than a nuisance in those places where it happened to seep to the surface. Now it is one of the most precious things on earth and wars are fought over it. The oil is called *petroleum,* from two Latin words meaning "rock oil."

Petroleum contains hundreds of different hydrocarbons. If it is to be useful, it must be refined. That is, it must be separated into different groups of hydrocarbons, each with its own special use. For instance, gasoline would be no good if it contained molecules with a fifteen-carbon chain. Such molecules would not evaporate easily and they would burn far too slowly. They would just choke the engine with gummy soot. So gasoline must consist of only a fraction of the whole petroleum mixture.[3]

The chief trick in petroleum refining depends on the fact that different hydrocarbons vaporize differently. The longer the carbon chain of a molecule, the harder it is to vaporize;

---

[3] The English refer to gasoline as *petrol,* which is, of course, short for petroleum. This is a poor name because gasoline and petroleum are not the same thing, but it is no poorer than our nickname "gas" which is short for gasoline.

more heat is required to turn it completely to vapor. A hydrocarbon with a long carbon chain, in other words, has a higher *boiling point* than one with a short carbon chain.

If just a little heat is applied to petroleum, the vapors of those molecules with very short carbon chains are produced. These vapors can be drawn off and allowed to cool into a liquid again. If more heat is applied, vapors with longer chains come off; the more heat, the longer the chain that is vaporized. The vapors are drawn off as they form and are then cooled until they liquefy. Each liquid is a different fraction of the original petroleum. This process is known as *fractional distillation.*[4]

The first fraction of petroleum to boil off is made up chiefly of pentanes and hexanes and is called *petroleum ether.* After that comes gasoline, which I've just been talking about. The next fraction is *kerosene.*

Fifty years ago or more, kerosene was quite an important substance because it was used to light the houses at night. Even today, in country districts (or in a city, when a hurricane or some other disaster has knocked out the power lines) kerosene lamps may be used. Petroleum was once important chiefly for its kerosene content. With the development of the electric light, kerosene went out, and with the development of the automobile, gasoline came in.

Today kerosene is cheaper than gasoline and special engines have been designed which can get along on kerosene. The Diesel engine does this. It is used in trucks, buses, locomotives, and ships. Efforts are being made these days to adapt such engines for use in ordinary automobiles, so kerosene may make a comeback yet.

The fraction after kerosene is *fuel oil.* This is being used more and more commonly to heat houses. As the hydrocarbon molecules get longer, less vapor is formed, and there is less danger of explosion. Fuel oil is much safer than gaso-

---

[4] Petroleum often contains hydrocarbons with very short chains that are gases to begin with. These are dissolved in the liquid portion of the oil, but when petroleum is drawn out of the earth, the gases come bubbling out. This is called *natural gas* and is made up mostly of methane. As I said earlier, this can be used in cooking food and in heating houses.

line to handle; yet it will burn easily enough in oil furnaces.

Nowadays, in refining petroleum, chemists are not content with its natural gasoline content. The petroleum is subjected to special processes designed to break up the long carbon-chain molecules into shorter pieces. In this way, molecules which would ordinarily be in the kerosene or fuel oil fractions end up in gasoline. This process is known as *cracking*. In one way or another, about half of each gallon of petroleum can be made into gasoline.

It is also possible to prepare gasoline from coal. Some grades of coal contain long-chain hydrocarbons which can be separated out. Their molecules can then be cracked down to the proper length. Even the solid coal itself, which is mostly carbon atoms, can be treated with hydrogen gas so as to form some gasoline.

More Fractions

It may seem that hydrocarbons are useful only because they will burn or explode to give heat, light, and power. This is not so. Hydrocarbons with molecules even larger than those in fuel oil burn with such difficulty that other uses become more important.

For instance, petroleum fractions with molecules larger than those in fuel oil are useful in cutting down friction. A film of such *lubricating oil*, placed between two moving surfaces, allows those surfaces to move past each other smoothly on a slippery cushion of hydrocarbon. A specially refined type of lubricating oil is *mineral oil*. This is sometimes taken internally so that a lubricating film may be formed on the walls of the intestines to ease the discomforts of constipation. Solids of various sort can be added to lubricating oil to thicken it to a blackish, semi-solid *lubricating grease*.

Petroleum fractions with molecules still more complicated than those of lubricating oils are no longer liquid at ordinary temperatures. They are solid or semi-solid. An example is *petrolatum* or *petroleum jelly* [5] which is used in ointments

[5] This may be more familiar to you under the name of *Vaseline*. The name, Vaseline, is an example of a *trade name*. This is a name given to a particular product by the company that manu-

or directly on the human skin for its softening and smoothing action.

The nature of the final fraction of petroleum depends on the particular oilfield from which the petroleum came. Sometimes, a remainder, made up mostly of carbon atoms, is left behind after refining. This is *petroleum coke*. Other times, a soft solid made up of very large hydrocarbon molecules (plus other types of molecules as well) is left behind. This is *petroleum asphalt*.

Asphalt is often used to surface roads. It was used for this purpose in ancient Babylon in 600 B.C. The first use in the United States was in 1870 in Newark, New Jersey. Now 800,000,000 miles of American streets and highways are so paved.

There is a famous asphalt "lake" in the Caribbean island of Trinidad, covering 115 acres, at least 285 feet deep in spots, and containing perhaps as much as 15 million tons of asphalt. This was probably once an ordinary petroleum deposit which was exposed to the open air through some unusual set of geological processes. All the liquid portions have been lost with the ages and only the asphalt is left.

Large hydrocarbon molecules, containing eighteen or more carbon atoms, can be separated from the solid fractions of petroleum. These are white solids, slippery to the touch, and easily melted. A mixture of these is called *paraffin wax*. Paraffin wax is a mind-its-own-business kind of substance. It is affected by very few chemicals and it bothers very few. It is *chemically inert*. The very word "paraffin" comes from two Latin words which can be roughly translated as "slight tendency to mix."

This standoffishness is useful. Paper coated with wax

---

factures it. Such a name is protected by law so that only one company may use it. Other companies, that may be marketing the identical product, must use a different name. Sometimes such a trade name becomes so well known that even chemists use it instead of the official chemical name of the product. Trade names should always be capitalized. Lately, it is even becoming customary to follow trade names with a special symbol ®, which means Registered.

(*wax-paper*) is often used as a wrapping for various kinds of food. Wax-paper is waterproof. It can't be penetrated by water; and water won't even wet it. If a drop of water touches it, it stays on the surface and can be easily wiped off. The containers in which milk is often sold are made of waxed cardboard.

Parraffin wax is used in the home preparation of fruit preserves or jellies. Melted paraffin is poured over the surface of the jelly in the jar. When it cools and hardens, it acts as a seal to keep out air and prevent molding and crystallization. Candles are often made of paraffin wax. Melted wax is allowed to solidify in a long column around a cotton cord called a wick. The end of the wick is then set on fire. The heat of the burning wick melts some of the wax near it and then cracks the long carbon-chains of the molecules in the melted wax into shorter chains. These shorter-chain molecules vaporize and burn. The heat of this burning melts more of the wax and supplies more vapor. In this way, little by little, the whole candle burns.

Oil and Water

I mentioned a while ago that paraffin wax is waterproof. Let's look into that a little bit.

As you know, substances like salt or sugar will *dissolve* and appear to vanish if placed in water. What happens is that the solid salt or sugar breaks up into single molecules (or parts of molecules) which then mix completely with the water. Salt and sugar are, for that reason, said to be *soluble* in water.

Hydrocarbons are *insoluble* in water. If gasoline and water are shaken together, for instance, and allowed to stand, they will separate again and form two layers. (The gasoline layer will be on top because, like all hydrocarbons and hydrocarbon mixtures, it is lighter than water.)

Water molecules and hydrocarbon molecules have different electrical properties. These properties depend upon the *electrons* in the various atoms that make up the molecule. Electrons are particles that are much smaller than atoms and occur within atoms. If the electrons are evenly distributed through the molecule, the electrical properties are like those in hydrocarbon. If they are unevenly distributed, the electrical properties are like those in water.

Substances with molecules that have electrical properties like those of water will dissolve in water, but not in hydrocarbon. Substances with molecules that have electrical properties like those of hydrocarbon will dissolve in hydrocarbon, but not in water. Like clings to like in this particular case. Opposites don't attract.

Salt and sugar have electrical properties like water. They dissolve in water.

The fats and oils we find in food are among the compounds that have molecules with the electrical properties of hydrocarbons. They dissolve in hydrocarbons.

All too frequently, clothing, tablecloths, or other fabrics are accidentally spotted by grease. Dabbing at the spots with water will have no effect. Hydrocarbon or some similar compound must be used. Moreover, the hydrocarbon to be used must not itself remain behind as a spot (and a smelly one, to boot). The trick then is to use a petroleum fraction with molecules made up of the shortest possible carbon chains. Then, when the spot is gone, the hydrocarbon molecules still in the fabric quickly turn to vapor and blow away, leaving nothing behind.

The liquid petroleum fraction with the smallest molecules is, as I mentioned earlier, petroleum ether. (This may be more familiar to you as "benzine." That, however, is an undesirable name. There is another, and much more important, substance called "benzene" and the two should not be confused.) This substance is quite commonly used in the home as a spot-remover.

Since this method of cleaning does not involve water, petroleum ether is an example of a *dry cleaner*. The main danger involved in its use is that it is even more inflammable than gasoline. There is always the risk of fire and explosion. When you use a petroleum ether dry cleaner, make sure there are no gas flames about—and don't smoke!

Chapter 2

A Shortage of Hydrogen

Two Bonds are Livelier than One

THERE ARE still a few variations left in the ways in which carbon atoms may be put together. In the structural formulas shown in Chapter 1, neighboring atoms were connected by single lines. Neighboring carbon atoms devoted just one of their four bonds to each other and saved their remaining three bonds for other atoms.

It is possible, however, that neighboring carbon atoms might be connected by two of their four bonds. This will leave each carbon atom with only two bonds to be used in other ways. The simplest such molecule is this:

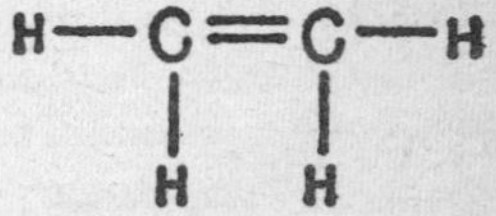

Figure 5—Ethylene

$$H-C=C-H$$

This is *ethylene*. Its molecule contains a *double bond*.

Compare the structural formula of ethylene with that of ethane in Chapter 1. The ethane molecule is made up of two carbon atoms and six hydrogen atoms. The ethylene molecule is made up of two carbon atoms and only four hydrogen atoms. The ethane molecule has all the hydrogen atoms it can hold. It is a *saturated hydrocarbon*. In ethylene there is a hydrogen shortage because an extra bond that might otherwise be used for hydrogen atoms is used to hold the carbon atoms together. Ethylene is an *unsaturated hydrocarbon*.

A long carbon chain can have a double bond anywhere along the line. If the chain is branched, the double bond might be in the branch. There can be more than one double bond in a molecule. Important compounds are known with a dozen or more double bonds in their molecules. Every different arrangement, every different location, means a different compound. (More isomers! More trillions of organic molecules!)

The carbon atom is most at ease when its four bonds stick out comfortably in four different directions. There is a certain amount of strain when two bonds are forced to line up between the same two carbon atoms. The result is that the double bond represents a kind of weak spot in the carbon chain. The chain is livelier at that point. Other chemicals will attack it just at the double bond. If the action is vigorous enough, the double bond may be broken completely and the chain will fall apart.

By noticing what happens when certain chemicals are added to an organic compound, chemists can tell whether a double bond is present or not. By breaking the chain and studying the pieces, they can tell just where in the chain the double bond was located.

Catalysts and Plastics

If a compound with a double bond is treated with hydrogen gas under the proper conditions, hydrogen atoms will add on to the double bond. That is, one of the two bonds between the carbon atoms will be broken. Each carbon atom will then use its newly available bond to hook on to a hydrogen atom. In this way, an unsaturated compound will become saturated. As I shall explain later, such *hydrogenations* are sometimes of importance to the housewife.

The reaction between an unsaturated compound and hydrogen gas is a very slow process if those two subtances are left to themselves. The chemist can hasten it, however, by adding to the mixture a small quantity of certain finely divided metals. The metal doesn't take part in the hydrogenation itself. It's just that the surface of the tiny metal particles seems to be an ideal place for the unsaturated compound and the hydrogen to combine. In the presence of the metal, therefore, the hydrogenation proceeds millions of times as rapidly as in its absence.

Any substance that hastens a reaction just by its presence, without getting used up in the process, is called a *catalyst*. Over the years, chemists have discovered numerous substances that can be used as catalysts for one type of chemical reaction or another. Without catalysts, our chemical industries would be stopped in their tracks.

The presence of the double bond can lead to other interesting results, too. If ethylene is heated to a high temperature and put under high pressure, two things happen. First, the high temperature breaks one of the two bonds between the carbon atoms. Then, because the ethylene molecules are pushed so closely together by the pressure, the newly available bonds can be easily used to link neighboring ethylene molecules. The result is a very long chain of thousands of carbon atoms all connected by single bonds. This compound is called *polyethylene* or *polythene*. (The prefix "poly" comes from a Greek word meaning "many" and is often used in chemical names.)

The polyethylene molecule is like a wax molecule except that its carbon chain is longer than that of a wax molecule. It is a cloudy white solid with a slippery feel. Polyethylene is not brittle, like wax, but is flexible and tough. And it is just as chemically inert as wax.

Wax will become soft from the heat of our hands. Polyethylene must be heated above the temperature of boiling water before it begins to soften. Once softened, though, it can be molded into any desired shape. If it is then cooled, it will keep its new shape indefinitely.

Any substance which can be molded into a permanent shape (either with heat or under pressure) is called a *plastic*. Polyethylene is an example.

Polyethylene has come into general use only since World War II, but already it is everywhere. Objects can be wrapped in polyethylene bags which are heat-sealed at the edges. (Two sheets of polyethylene heated at the edges, will melt together and form an airtight, watertight seal.) Wastepaper baskets, laundry baskets, sink-mats, bags, containers, and many other objects are being made of it. Polyethylene is light, and is kept clean easily. It will not break, crack or chip. It is not affected by water or most of the other materials one is likely to find in the house. It is an example of a useful substance which did not exist until it was manufactured by chemists.

Many types of molecules, usually unsaturated, can be made to hook together into long chains in this way. Polystyrene, also called *distrene,* is another plastic, that starts with an unsaturated hydrocarbon, *styrene,* which is somewhat more complicated than ethylene. In general, the single molecule that one starts with is called a *monomer* (from Greek words meaning "one part"). The long chain built out of the monomer is a *polymer* (from Greek words meaning "many parts"). Ethylene, for instance, is said to *polymerize* to form polyethylene. Usually, a compound can be considered a polymer when its molecule contains at least 200 carbon atoms.

Natural Colors

One very important unsaturated hydrocarbon is *isoprene* and here is its structural formula:

Figure 6—Isoprene

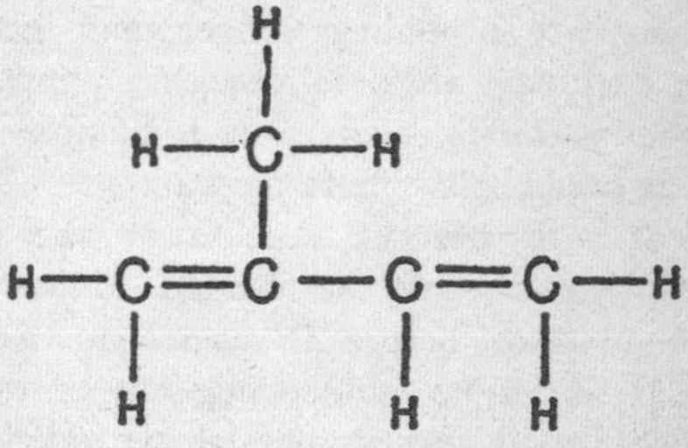

Isoprene, as you see, is a five-carbon molecule with a branch in the chain. Also, it has two double bonds, with a single bond between them. This is very important. Whenever double bonds and single bonds take turns along a carbon chain, like this: —C=C—C=C—C=C—C=C—, the double bonds are said to be *conjugate.*

Conjugate double bond arrangements are more stable than double bonds arranged otherwise. Organic compounds that have long chains of carbon atoms with several double bonds included, usually have these double bonds arranged in conjugate form.

Like ethylene, isoprene molecules can be made to join together. In fact, many of the natural products found in plant tissues have molecules that look as if they were formed by joining together a number of isoprene molecules in various ways. The resulting molecules have ten carbon atoms, or fifteen, or twenty, or more, depending on the number of isoprene molecules that have been joined. Molecules built out of isoprene units in this way are called *terpenes,* because such compounds were first located in turpentine.

One of the most important terpens is *carotene,* which contains forty carbon atoms (eight isoprene units joined). Carotene was first found in carrots; hence its name.

Carotene contains eleven double bonds and these are conjugate. That brings up an interesting point. A compound with several conjugate double bonds is usually colored. Carotene is colored and is responsible for many of the colors in nature. Solid carotene is red, but when it is dissolved in fat, it can be orange or yellow depending on the amount dissolved. Carrots and sweet potatoes are orange-colored because of the carotene they contain. Carotene is also responsible for the yellow color of butter and egg yolk. Animal fat that contains carotene, such as chicken fat, is yellow. Animal fat without carotene, such as lard, is white.

Carotene is sometimes even responsible for the color of human skin. Some of it is dissolved in the fatty layer under the skin. The people of East Asia have enough carotene under their skins to give it a yellowish cast.

There are other colors in nature for which compounds like carotene are responsible. The red color of tomatoes and of boiled lobster shells are caused by carotene-like compounds. The compound in tomatoes is called *lycopene* from the Latin name for the tomato plant.

Have you noticed that all the saturated hydrocarbons I mentioned in Chapter 1 had names that ended in "ane" while the unsaturated hydrocarbons mentioned in this chapter have names ending in "ene"? Chemists always try to make logical rules for naming organic compounds. Their most ambitious attempt in this direction was at an international meeting of chemists held in Geneva, Switzerland in 1892. A system called the *Geneva nomenclature* was set up. One of the rules was "ane" endings for saturated hydrocarbons and "ene" for hydrocarbons with double bonds. Every organic compound with a molecule of known structure has an official Geneva name. However, the names actually used are not always the official ones. For one thing, some organic chemicals were named well before 1892 and people got used to those old names and wouldn't change them. For another, the Geneva name is sometimes long and complicated so that chemists think of a shorter name for convenience and then stick to it.

The South American Toy

Certain tropical plants produce a kind of milky sap called *latex*. This will ooze out if the outer layers of the stem are cut. This latex is made up mostly of microscopic particles of polymerized isoprene floating in water. The latex can be treated with certain chemicals which cause the tiny particles to clump together and settle out as *raw rubber*. (Rubber is so called because one of the first uses to which it was put was to rub out pencil marks. The British call it *India rubber* because they got their first supplies from the West Indies.)

The rubber tree, which is the most important source of the substance, was originally native to Brazil. Indeed, rubber was unknown to Europe until Columbus discovered South American Indian children using pieces of rubber as bouncing toys. The French name for rubber, *caoutchouc*, comes from the original Indian word, which meant "weeping wood." Rubber trees were eventually transplanted to the Malayan peninsula in Southeast Asia and grown on plantations there. Malaya is now a much more important rubber-producing region than Brazil.

Raw rubber is soft and sticky, particularly in hot weather. In cold weather, it gets as stiff as a board. For this reason, early raincoats (called mackintoshes after the Scotsman—Charles Macintosh—who first smeared rubber on cloth to make it waterproof) were only useful part of the time.

In 1838, however, Charles Goodyear, an American, discovered, quite by accident, that if raw rubber were heated with a bit of sulfur, the product would resist heat and cold much better. It remained non-sticky and flexible in winter and summer alike. Rubber so treated is called *vulcanized rubber*. Almost all rubber in use to day is vulcanized. When enough sulfur is added, hard rubber (sometimes called *ebonite* or *vulcanite*) is formed. This was used quite a bit in the days before modern plastics became popular.

(Such an important discovery ought to have made Goodyear rich. It would certainly have done so in a story book. Unfortunately, things don't always work out so neatly. Goodyear was in debt all his life and ran his first experiments on rubber while in debtors' prison. After that, patent troubles of one sort or another kept him poor and when he died in 1860, he was in debt for $600,000.)

Rubber has really come into its own since the development of the automobile. It is a tough substance that takes much longer to wear out from rubbing against the road than any metal would. It is elastic and, used in tires, helps give a smooth ride. (Have you ever ridden in a wagon with metal-rimmed wooden wheels? Imagine one of those going sixty miles an hour.) Furthermore, rubber tires flatten against the road and, with the aid of gouges called "treads," grip the road and resist skidding.

The industrial nations have become more and more dependent on rubber for tires as well as for many other uses. Their main supplies come from far-away Malaya. This is, naturally, a ticklish situation, especially in war time, when the need for rubber is increased. (The first objects to be rationed in the United States during the World War II crisis were automobile tires.)

Many attempts have been made to produce an artificial rubber in order that nations might not find themselves cut off from their rubber supplies in time of war. You might think that the logical thing to do would be to take some isoprene and treat it in such a way as to polymerize it. Well, that was one of the first things tried but it didn't work.

The isoprene molecules in rubber, you see, are joined in one particular way. For many years, chemists could get the isoprene molecules to join, but not in the right way. The artificial product turned out to be more like *gutta percha*. This is a substance produced by certain Malayan trees. It is also an isoprene polymer, but it is not elastic and so it is useless as a rubber substitute.

Other unsaturated hydrocarbons were used and elastic

polymers (called *elastomers*) were obtained. An artificial rubber made from *butadiene* (which has a molecule like isoprene without the little one-carbon branch) has been used in Germany and the Soviet Union since the early 1930s, for instance. It goes under the trade name of *Buna*.

Organic compounds that are not hydrocarbons have also been built up into artificial rubbers. Most of them have their good points but none seem to have the all-round virtues of natural rubber.

Within the last year or so, finally, chemists have learned to duplicate rubber itself in the laboratory. It was a question of finding just the proper catalyst and this they have now done. (Brand-new useful polymers of all sorts may lie just ahead as the result of these new catalysts.)

Rubber, a hydrocarbon, will dissolve in kerosene and in similar liquids. Such solutions are the *rubber cements*.

Three Bonds Are Still Livelier

Two carbon atoms can be held together by three bonds, a so-called *triple bond*. If this happens, each carbon atom has only one bond left free for attachment to another atom. An example of a compound with a molecule that contains such an arrangement is this:

$$H \text{—} C \equiv C \text{—} H \qquad \textit{Figure 7—Acetylene}$$

This compound is called *acetylene*.[1]

Carbon chains with triple bonds are like carbon chains with double bonds, only more so. Acetylene has fewer hydrogen atoms than ethylene (only two of them) and is therefore more unsaturated.

The triple bond is under even more strain than the double bond. (A "quadruple bond," by the way, is completely impossible.) It takes considerable energy to hold the triple bond in place. When acetylene burns, the triple

[1] Here is an example of a chemical name not based on the Geneva nomenclature. The Geneva congress agreed to have triple-bond hydrocarbons named with a "yne" ending. In most cases, this is done. Acetylene should be called "ethyne" but it isn't and it won't be and that's all there is to it.

bond is broken and all that energy is changed into heat. As a result, the flame of burning acetylene is hotter than the flame of burning ethane or burning ethylene.

This heat is made use of in the *oxyacetylene torch*. This device brings a stream of oxygen and one of acetylene together. When the mixture is set on fire, the resulting flame is used for welding and cutting metals. Such a torch will melt its way through steel as though it were so much butter.

The strain built up by triple bonds has another result. Compounds containing triple bonds will sometimes explode. Their molecules break at the triple bond and become simpler molecules without triple bonds. The energy released by the elimination of the triple bond causes the force of the explosion.

This is particularly true if the carbon of the triple bond is attached to a copper or silver atom rather than to a hydrogen atom. Such *metal acetylides* are more dangerous than explosives like methane. Methane will explode only if mixed with air or oxygen. Metal acetylides don't need the outside help of any other molecules. Even after mixture with air, methane won't explode unless it is heated. Metal acetylides don't need heat. Sometimes just the shock of a light blow is sufficient.

One metal acetylide that is not explosive is *calcium carbide*. Its molecule contains two carbon atoms held together by a triple bond and both connected by the spare bond to a single calcium atom. (Calcium is a silvery metal. Its atoms are found in limestone and in bones. Substances containing calcium atoms in their molecules are quite common in the soil about us.)

If calcium carbide makes contact with water, the water molecules combine with the calcium atom and leave hydrogen atoms in its place. In this way, acetylene is formed. Back in the days when bicycles were very popular, and before battery-powered electric lights came into popular use, canisters of calcium carbide were sometimes used for lighting purposes. Water was allowed to drip into the canister slowly and the acetylene which was produced fed a flame that acted as a bicycle headlight. It was also used in the headlights of the very early automobiles.

In building up complicated molecules for our uses, the chemist likes to begin with simple compounds that are as cheap and common as possbile. Acetylene is one of the most important of the chemist's starting materials. The fact that the triple bond is extra lively and allows the acetylene to react with a number of chemicals makes it all the more useful.

Chapter 3

Rings, One and Many

The Battle Against Pain

What is to prevent the two ends of a carbon chain from joining to form a closed ring? Nothing at all. It happens all the time.

The simplest ring, one with three carbons only, has a structural formula that is easily drawn, thus:

Figure 8—Cyclopropane

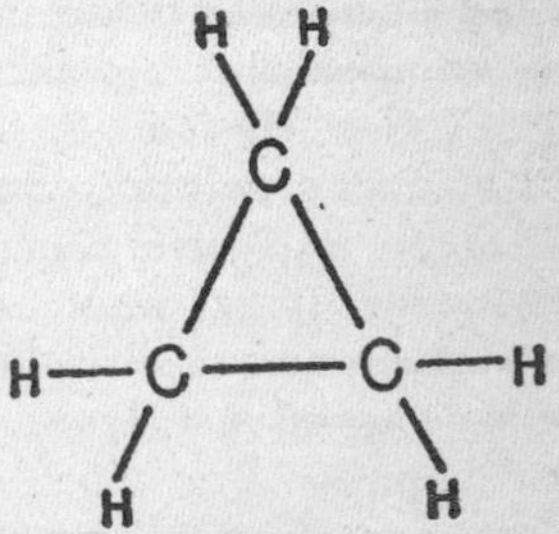

The ordinary three-carbon hydrocarbon is propane, as you may remember. With the carbon atoms joined in a ring, the molecule is called *cyclopropane*. (The prefix "cyclo" shows that the carbon atoms in the molecule have formed a cycle, or circle.) In general, compounds containing rings of atoms are called *cyclic compounds*. Those without rings are *acyclic compounds*. (The prefix "a" is taken from Greek and means "not.")

Cyclopropane is an *anesthetic* (from a Greek word meaning "no feeling"). That is, when it is inhaled under the proper conditions, it will cause a person to lose the ability to feel pain. Usually, he loses consciousness, too.

The anesthetic does this by acting upon our nerves. Each nerve is surrounded, in part, by a *myelin sheath*. This is composed of molecules that are fairly similar to hydrocarbons in their electrical properties. The nerve fiber, when in action, carries a very small electric current, and the myelin sheath acts as an insulator.

When the lungs are filled with hydrocarbons (or similar compounds), some of the hydrocarbon molecules are absorbed into the bloodstream. From the bloodstream, they enter the various tissues of the body. They mix most easily with those parts of the body made up of molecules that resemble the hydrocarbons electrically. Therefore, the myelin sheaths are ideal. The hydrocarbon molecules accumulate in the myelin sheath. Once the myelin sheath is loaded with these molecules, nerve action stops. The nerve is, somehow, short-circuited. The brain no longer receives impulses such as pain which are carried by the nerves.

The use of anesthetics can be risky. For one thing, when inhaling an anesthetic, a patient must also inhale oxygen or he will suffocate. He must therefore be given just the proper mixture of anesthetic and oxygen to inhale. This mixture is usually highly explosive. For that reason, no smoking is allowed nearby, sparks must be guarded against, and so on.

Also, there must be neither too much nor too little anesthetic. The heart, lungs, and other vital organs are run by nerve impulses. Too much anesthetic will mean that the nerves that control those organs may also be short-circuited. If the situation is not corrected immediately, the patient will die.

On the other hand, once the patient is unconscious and is allowed to breathe ordinary air, the anesthetic slowly leaks out of the myelin sheaths, back into the lungs, and out of the body. After a while, the myelin sheaths are back to normal and the patient revives. If the operation is not over, he must be given additional anesthetic.

For all these reasons, anesthetics are administered in modern hospitals only by trained people who must use great skill and caution.

Hydrocarbon gases of different types vary in their anesthetic properties. Ethylene and acetylene are fairly strong anesthetics, stronger than the straight-chain saturated hydrocarbons. The hydrocarbon which is the strongest anesthetic of all, however, is cyclopropane, which I mentioned at the beginning of this section. It was first used as an anesthetic in 1929 and has stayed in use ever since.

One of the advantages of both cyclopropane and ethylene is that they can be mixed with considerable oxygen without losing strength. This reduces the chances of suffocating the patient. On the other hand, it makes the mixture particularly explosive.

Hexagons

You can have a ring of four carbon atoms (*cyclobutane*), five carbon atoms (*cyclopentane*), six carbon atoms (*cyclohexane*), or more. Carbon atoms form rings of five or six atoms (particularly six) most often. For instance, most of the terpene hydrocarbons contain six-carbon rings as part of the molecule. Carotene has six-carbon rings at each end of its long molecule.

The most important six-carbon ring is that which makes up the molecule of *benzene*. Compare its formula (on the right) with that of cyclohexane (on the left):

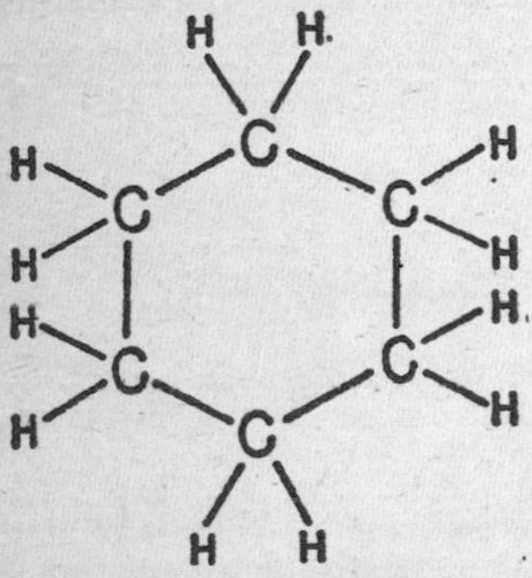

Figure 9—Cyclohexane 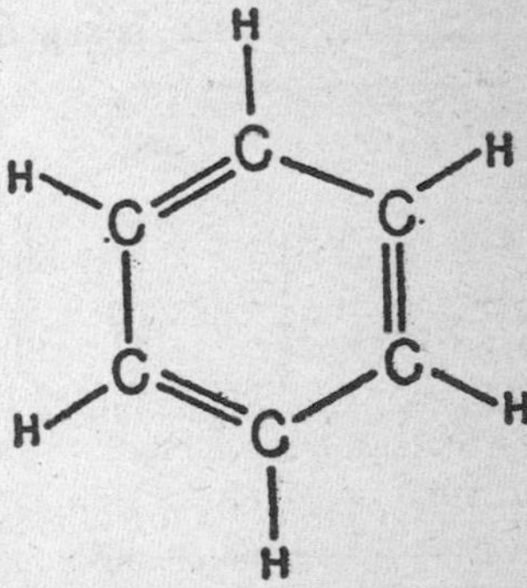   Figure 10—Benzene

Benzene has three double bonds. These alternate with single bonds so that benzene contains conjugate double bonds. This makes benzene rather inactive; less active than cyclohexane, for instance.[1] The benzene ring takes less energy to form. The result is that a great many organic compounds contain the benzene ring as part of their molecules. So many compounds do, in fact, that chemists usually place all such compounds in a special class and call them *aromatic compounds*. The first few natural compounds found to belong to this class had a definite, fairly pleasant aroma; hence the name. However, that should not be taken too seriously. It is impossible to tell aromatic compounds from other organic compounds just by the smell.

In writing formulas, chemists often save time by representing rings of carbon atoms as simple geometrical figures. For instance, cyclohexane is written as a six-sided figure (called a hexagon), thus:

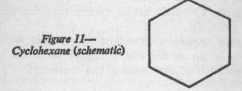

Figure 11—
Cyclohexane (schematic)

and benzene is a hexagon with the double bonds marked, thus:

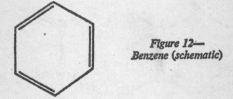

Figure 12—
Benzene (schematic)

[1] Ever since the formula for benzene was first worked out (by Kekulé), organic chemists have puzzled over its details. In many ways, the benzene molecule behaves as though the double bonds aren't really there. (After all the double bonds ought to make benzene *more,* not less, active than cyclo-hexane.) Modern theories of atomic behavior have finally given chemists a fairly satisfactory answer. The theories are too complicated to go into here but they involve notions of partial or fractional bonds. Thus, the six carbon atoms of the benzene ring can be looked upon as being connected by six equal "one-and-a-half" bonds which are less active than either single or double bonds.

If you ever have to make sense out of formulas containing these hexagons, or other figures like them, just remember two simple rules:

First: a carbon atom must be placed at each angle of the figure;

Second: any spare bonds not involved in forming the ring must be filled with hydrogen atoms. (If any atoms other than hydrogen atoms are involved, they are shown in the geometrical formulas so that you know they are there.)

It is these geometric figures that make most organic formulas look so complicated and frightening to people who aren't used to them. Actually, if you remember the two rules, you have no trouble with them. Still, as far as this book is concerned, I will use geometrical figures only when I absolutely have to.

More Power in Gasoline

A carbon atom (or a chain of carbon atoms) can be attached to one or more of the atoms making up a ring. Such an attached atom or atoms is called a *side-chain*. The simplest of such aromatic compounds is one in which a single carbon is attached to a benzene ring, as follows:

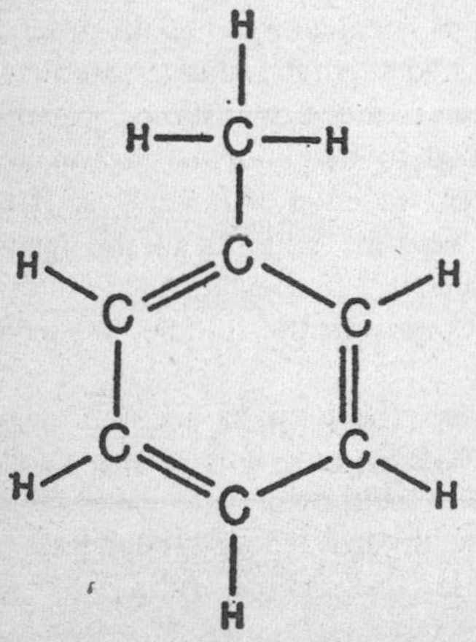

Figure 13—Toluene

The side-chain in this compound consists of a carbon atom to which three hydrogen atoms are attached. It is, so to speak, a methane molecule with one hydrogen atom missing. Such a side-chain is therefore called a *methyl group*. A benzene ring with a methyl group attached is called *toluene*.

What if there are two methyl groups attached to a benzene ring? Here there is an opportunity for isomerism, since there are three different ways in which two methyl groups can be attached to a benzene ring. The easiest way to show this to you is to use a hexagon to represent the benzene ring and attach little dashes to indicate the two methyl groups, thus:

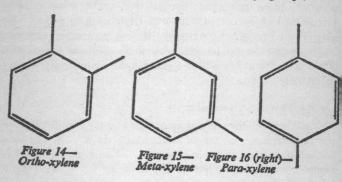

Figure 14—
Ortho-xylene

Figure 15—
Meta-xylene

Figure 16 (right)—
Para-xylene

Any compound with a molecule consisting of a benzene ring and two methyl groups is called *xylene*.[2] In order to show the exact position of the two methyl groups, however, certain prefixes are attached to the name. For instance, when the two methyl groups are attached to neighboring carbon atoms, as in the hexagon on the left, we have *ortho-xylene*. If they are on opposite ends of the benzene ring, as in the hexagon on the right, we have *para-xylene*. If they have an intermediate arrangement, as in the hexagon in the middle, we have *meta-xylene*.

Sometimes, to save space, the prefixes are abbreviated and the names are written: *o*-xylene, *m*-xylene, and *p*-xylene, with the initials written in italics as shown.

These simple aromatic hydrocarbons—benzene, toluene, and the xylenes—increase the octane rating of gasoline.

---

[2] Chemical names starting with "x" are pronounced as though they start with a "z." This is "zylene," therefore; not "ksylene" or "exylene."

Gasoline containing them is sometimes called *aromatic fuel* and sometimes *aviation gasoline* because it is used for airplanes. The "aromatics" are now also used in the new "superpremium" gasolines on the market for use in late-model automobiles.

Petroleum usually contains aromatic hydrocarbons along with the other varieties. The exact amount varies according to the area in which the oil well is located. Some samples of petroleum from Borneo have as much as 40 per cent of aromatic hydrocarbon.

Aromatic hydrocarbons can also be obtained from bituminous coal. Such coal, commonly called "soft coal," is 70 to 80 percent carbon. The remaining 20 to 30 percent is hydrogen and organic compounds (the latter being mostly hydrocarbon). If such coal is heated in the absence of air (to keep it from burning) everything but the carbon is driven off. The carbon that remains is called *coke*.

The material driven off from bituminous coal by the heat is partly in the form of a gas called *coke-oven gas*. This is made up mostly of hydrogen and methane. However, a small percentage of it consists of vapors of more complicated molecules. These can be separated out as a liquid called *light oil*. This is mostly benzene, toluene, and the xylenes. Every ton of bituminous coal will yield nearly three gallons of this light oil.

More benzene, in fact, is derived from coal than from petroleum. Benzene is produced in enough quantity so that it serves as a very important starting material for chemists who wish to build up more complicated molecules.

Moth Balls and Cancer

Two or more rings of carbon atoms can join up like the cells in a honeycomb. Such combinations are said to consist of *fused rings*.

A simple fused-ring compound is *naphthalene*. Its molecule is made up of a combination of two benzene rings. I will show you the formula here, both in full and in geometrical shorthand.

Unlike benzene, toluene, and the xylenes, which are liquids at ordinary temperatures, naphthalene is a white solid. Its most familiar use, at one time, was to keep moths away from clothes. It was placed among the clothes in closed trunks and closets, usually in the form of small, white spheres called mothballs. These gave off vapors that slowly filled the air within those trunks and closets. Apparently, moths found such vapors unpleasant and stayed away. Nowadays, naphthalene has been replaced by more effective compounds.

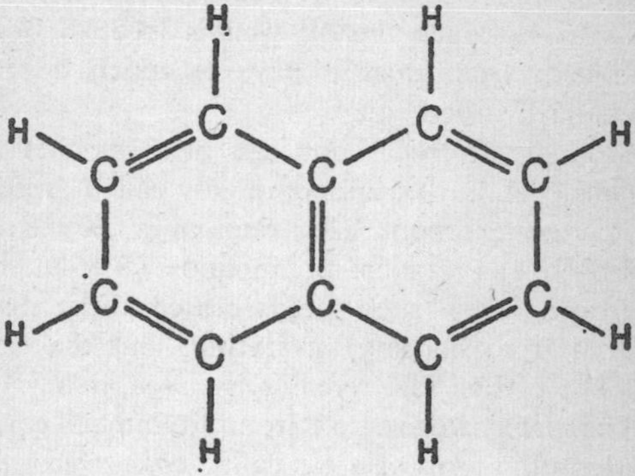

Figure 17—
Naphthalene

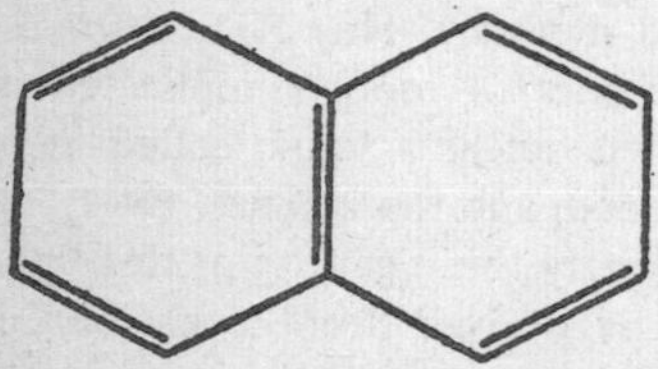

Figure 18
Naphthalene (schematic)

Some naphthalene is found in the light oil fraction of bituminous coal. More of it, however, is found in another fraction of that same coal. After the coal has been heated and the coke-oven gas fraction has been driven off, some organic material still remains in the coal. Still stronger heating drives this off, too, and it is collected as a thick black liquid called coal tar. A ton of bituminous coal will yield about sixty pounds of coal tar.

This coal tar is about ten percent napthalene. The rest is largely made up of other hydrocarbons with rather complicated fused-ring compounds. Compounds with three, four, five, or even more fused rings have been isolated from coal tar and some of these are quite dangerous.

In 1914 Japanese chemists first found that certain portions of the coal-tar mixture of compounds could produce cancer in animals if the coal-tar was applied to their skin for a long enough time. In 1930, British chemists discovered a particular hydrocarbon, made up of five fused benzene rings, which could be obtained from coal tar and which could cause cancer. Such a cancer-causing compound is called a *carcinogen*. Since 1930, dozens of carcinogens have been discovered in coal-tar and elsewhere.

(Recently, small amounts of carcinogens have been found in the smoke of burning tobacco. Doctors are wondering if there is a connection between cigarette-smoking and lung cancer, because lung cancer has become a good deal more common than it used to be.)

A particularly important combination of fused rings forms what we may call the *steroid nucleus*. I won't draw the detailed arrangement of atoms, but only the geometric pattern of the rings:

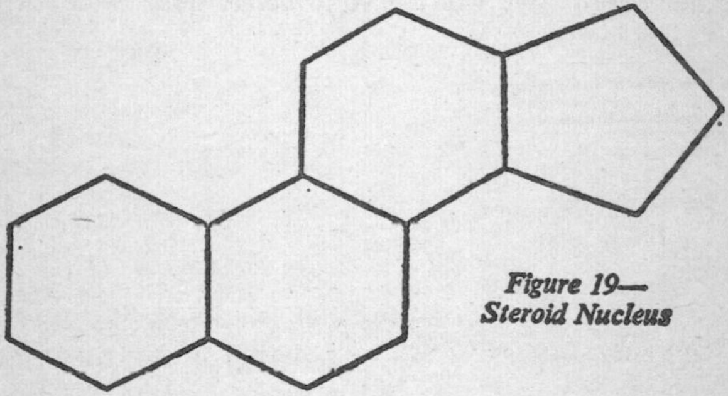

Figure 19—
Steroid Nucleus

There are four rings. Three of them are six-carbon rings arranged in a bent line. (Three six-carbon rings so arranged form a *phenanthrene* group.) The fourth ring, the one on the upper right, contains only five carbon atoms. A large number of compounds containing this pattern of rings have been found in living tissue. Some are exceptionally important, too. This class of compounds is referred to as the *steroids*.

An example of a steroid hydrocarbon is *20-methylcholanthrene*. This has a molecule containing the steroid nucleus, plus an additional ring, nine double bonds, and a methyl side-chain.[3] The interesting thing about methylcholanthrene is that it is one of the most dangerous carcinogens known. Since some of the important compounds of the body also have a steroid nucleus as part of their molecules, chemists wonder if these might not be converted, occasionally, to something like 20-methyl-cholanthrene. They wonder if this might account for the development of cancer in a person. It seems unlikely, but they have not yet entirely ruled out the possibility.

[3] The Geneva nomenclature provides a system for numbering the carbon atoms in chains and rings. A name such as 20-methyl-cholanthrene indicates that the methyl group is attached to carbon atom number 20. Of course, you have to learn the numbering system in order to understand the formula from the name and, frankly, I have seen even experienced chemists grow confused in their numberings. We won't have to bother much with the numbers in this book.

Chapter 4

The Salt-Formers

Introducing New Atoms

UNTIL NOW, I have been talking about organic compounds with molecules made up of only carbon and hydrogen atoms. Now it is time to introduce other kinds of atoms.

To begin with, there is a group of elements called the *halogens*. There are four important members of this group: *fluorine, chlorine, bromine,* and *iodine*. Fluorine is a pale-green gas, very poisonous and very active. In fact, fluorine is the most active chemical known. It will tear away at almost any molecule with which it comes in contact, substituting its own atoms for some of those already in the molecule.

Chlorine is a yellow-green gas, also active and poisonous, though less so than flourine. Bromine is a dark-red liquid and iodine is a slate-grey solid.[1]

Although these substances are poisonous in themselves, their atoms can form part of the molecules of non-poisonous compounds. An atom of chlorine, for example, will combine with an atom of sodium[2] to form *sodium chloride,* or *table salt*. Sodium chloride is certainly not poisonous. Quite the contrary. It is essential to life.

Fluorine, bromine, and iodine also combine with sodium and each forms a compound that has the appearance of salt. (These other "salts" are more or less poisonous, however.) The very word "halogen," in fact, comes from Greek words meaning "salt-former."

In organic compounds, the various halogen atoms behave

[1] You may be familiar with something called "iodine" which is a brown-red liquid. That is actually "tincture of iodine." It is iodine dissolved in a mixture of alcohol and water.

[2] *Sodium* is a soft, silvery metal. It is very active and is dangerous in itself but forms part of very common, useful compounds. A metal very like sodium which I will also have occasion to mention now and then is *potassium*.

much like hydrogen atoms. Like the hydrogen atom, each can form a bond with only one other atom.

The chemical symbols for fluorine and iodine are the initial letters of the names. Fluorine is symbolized as F, iodine as I. Unfortunately, we can't do the same for chlorine. The symbol, C, represents carbon. The symbol for chlorine must be something different, and it is Cl. The letter B is the symbol for the element, boron, so the symbol for bromine must be different. It is Br.

Most elements, as a matter of fact, have symbols made up of two letters. The first is generally the initial letter of the name (usually of the English name, sometimes of the German or Latin name). The second letter comes from the body of the name. The first letter is always capitalized; the second is always lower-case. The symbol for chlorine, for instance, is never CL or cl. It is always Cl.

Of the four halogens, chlorine is the most common and its occurrence in organic compounds has been most studied.

Safe, but Dangerous

Let's begin with something simple. Suppose all the hydrogen atoms in a methane molecule are replaced by chlorine atoms, thus:

Figure 20—Carbon Tetrachloride

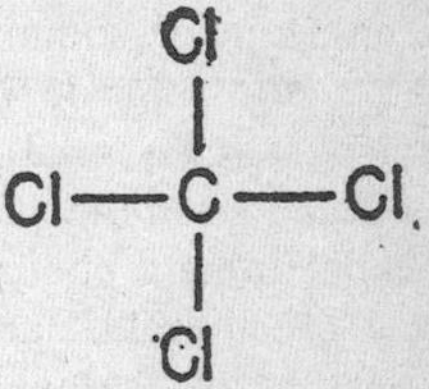

$$Cl - C - Cl$$

with Cl above and Cl below the central C.

This is *carbon tetrachloride*. (The prefix "tetra" is from the Greek word for "four.") Sometimes the compound is called "carbon tet" for short.

Carbon tetrachloride is different from methane in some ways, thanks to those chlorine atoms. Methane is a gas at room temperatures, but carbon tetrachloride is a liquid. Hydrocarbons in general are only about four-fifths as heavy as water, but carbon tetrachloride is 1½ times as heavy.

The most important fact is this: as chlorine atoms replace

hydrogen atoms, the compound becomes less inflammable. Carbon tetrachloride, with no hydrogen atoms in the molecule, will not burn at all. In fact, carbon tetrachloride is used in some kinds of fire extinguishers. When carbon tetrachloride is sprayed on a fire, the heat of the flame easily converts the liquid to a vapor.[3] This vapor is over five times as heavy as air so it doesn't blow away easily. It hugs the fire and keeps oxygen away. Since the carbon tetrachloride will not burn and will not support the burning of other substances, the fire must go out.

There is one catch, however, carbon tetrachloride vapors are quite poisonous. For this reason, using it as a fire-extinguisher in a poorly ventilated room is risky.

Carbon tetrachloride will mix with fatty substances as easily and quickly as hydrocarbons will. It, too, can be used as a dry cleaner and spot remover, and it frequently is. The most common trade-name for carbon tetrachloride dry cleaner is Carbona. Carbon tetrachloride is more expensive than petroleum ether or other hydrocarbon dry cleaners. But it has the great safety advantage of being non-inflammable, and can be used without fear of fire or explosion. However, you must remember that it is dangerous in another way. Watch out for the vapors. Make sure there is good ventilation when you are removing grease spots.

Not all the hydrogen atoms in methane need be replaced by chlorine atoms. Suppose only three are, thus:

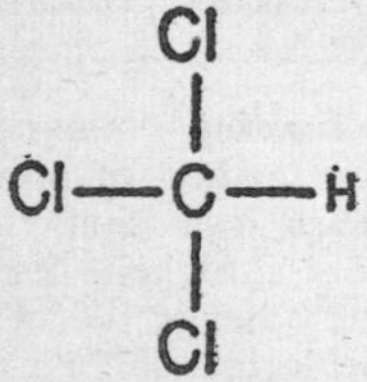

Figure 21—Chloroform

[3] Scientists use the *Centigrade scale* in measuring temperature. On this scale, the freezing point of water is zero degrees; written 0° C. Room temperature is about 25° C. and the boiling point of water is 100° C. The boiling point of carbon tetrachloride is 77° C. so you see that it will boil and become a vapor more easily than water will. Temperatures lower than the freezing point of water are written with a negative sign. Thus, methane boils at a

This is *chloroform*,[4] and it is perhaps the most familiar chlorine-containing compound, at least by name, to the general public.

Almost all of us have read adventure stories in which someone is knocked out by having a handkerchief soaked in chloroform forced over his or her nose. This is not just make-believe. Chloroform is a powerful anesthetic and has been used as such for over a century. A British physician, James Simpson, first used it on patients in 1847. Later on, he used it on Queen Victoria to ease the pains of childbirth for her. There was some opposition to this because a number of people thought that God meant human beings to suffer pain and that it was wicked to interfere with His plans. They quoted the Bible to prove this since in *Genesis* 3:16, God tells Eve: "In sorrow thou shalt bring forth childen."

However, Dr. Simpson pointed out that when God created Eve out of Adam's rib, He used a kind of anesthesia: "And the Lord God caused a deep sleep to fall upon Adam, and he slept: and he took one of his ribs, and closed up the flesh instead thereof." (*Genesis* 2:21.) This won the argument and the fact that Queen Victoria used anesthesia went a long way toward making its use respectable.

However, chloroform didn't remain respectable even if anesthetics in general did. Its great advantage over other anesthetics is that it is practically non-inflammable. Its great disadvantage is that it is quite poisonous, more so than most other anesthetics. Nowadays, it is practically never used if any other anesthetic is available. Doctors prefer to take the

---

temperature 161 degrees below the freezing point of water and this is written —161° C. The common method of measuring temperature in this country is the *Fahrenheit scale*. Sometimes, for the sake of familiarity, I will put the Fahrenheit temperature in parentheses. Thus, the boiling point of water is 100° C. (212° F.) and the boiling point of carbon tetrachloride is 77° C. (171° F.).

[4] You may have noticed that I don't always tell you where the name of a compound comes from. Sometimes, I don't know myself; or I know but don't think the details are worth explaining. At other times, the name cannot be understood completely until other compounds are discussed later on in the book. This is true of chloroform and a few other compounds I have mentioned before this.

chance of explosions and fires rather than risk the damage chloroform might do to the patient.

Freezing Skin and Killing Bugs

Any hydrocarbon can have its hydrogens replaced by chlorine atoms. Ethane, for instance, can have one hydrogen atom in its molecule replaced by a chlorine atom. The resulting compound is *ethyl chloride*.[5]

Ethyl chloride is a low-boiling liquid. Its boiling point is only 13° C. (55° F.). This means that it is a liquid in winter and a gas in summer.

Doctors keep ethyl chloride in little vessels with narrow sealed tips to keep it from evaporating. When they want to use it, they open a special valve. The heat of the doctor's hand then turns some of the liquid into a gas and the gas pressure forces the rest of the liquid out through the valve in a fine spray.

This spray is directed onto a spot on the patient's skin where some minor infection requires a moment of surgery. The liquid boils at once as it touches the warm skin. It boils so quickly that it withdraws a great deal of heat from the skin.[6] The skin undergoes a kind of frost-bite, turns white, and loses all feeling temporarily. If the doctor then works quickly, before the skin has a chance to warm up again, he can cut into the infected area and do what needs to be done, with the patient feeling no pain. A substance that causes a part of the body to lose feeling without affecting the rest of the body is a *local anesthetic*.

Aromatic compounds can also contain chlorine atoms. A

[5] I have already said that methane minus a hydrogen atom is called a methyl group. The same can be said about any hydrocarbon. Ethane minus a hydrogen atom is an ethyl group. In the same way you can have a propyl group, a butyl group, an isobutyl group and so on.

[6] It takes heat to convert a liquid to a gas; that is, to make it evaporate. Put a drop of water on your skin and blow on it. Some of the water evaporates, taking the heat from your skin for the purpose. The skin under the drop of water will feel colder than the dry skin about it. If, instead of water, you use a liquid that evaporates more quickly, like carbon tetrachloride, your skin will feel still colder. Ethyl chloride carries things to an extreme.

molecule of benzene can contain a chlorine atom in place of one of its hydrogen atoms, or in place of all six for that matter. A benzene molecule minus one hydrogen atom is referred to as a *phenyl group*[7] and one minus two hydrogen atoms is a *phenylene group*. Therefore, a benzene ring with two chlorine atoms replacing hydrogen atoms at opposite ends of the ring is called *para-phenylene dichloride*.[8] (The prefix, "di," is from a Greek word meaning "two.") Para-phenylene dichloride is an *insecticide*; that is, an insect-killer.[9] The housewife is familiar with it these days since it has largely replaced naphthalene as the substance out of which mothballs or mothflakes are made.

A more famous insecticide is the compound familiarly known as *DDT*. This was first put out as an insecticide by a Swiss firm in 1942 and since World War II it has become very common. Insect sprays used in the house nowadays almost always contain this compound. (DDT is poisonous to humans as well as to insects so it must be used carefully. It is not as poisonous, however, as old-fashioned insect sprays that contained lead or arsenic. By 1947, however, houseflies were developing resistance to DDT and newer insecticides had to be used.)

The term DDT is an example of how people, even chemists, abbreviate the long chemical names of compounds when they have to use those names frequently. (It's like saying UN instead of United Nations or USA instead of United States of America.) A longer name for DDT is *dichlorodiphenyltri-*

---

[7] You might expect it would be called a "benzyl group" but it isn't. A *benzyl group* is the name given to a molecule of toluene with one hydrogen atom missing from its side-chain. This doesn't sound logical, but I must admit that chemists are sometimes illogical and nothing can be done about it.

[8] It can also be called *para-dichlorobenzene,* which is another logical name for it. It often happens that a chemical compound can be called by more than one name. Chloroform, for instance, could be called "trichloromethane." Chemists get used to this situation just as you do to hearing our country called "The United States," "America," "Columbia," and "Uncle Sam."

[9] Insects aren't the only things we want to do away with. Mankind now makes use of chemicals to kill weeds, rats, and other forms of life that are harmful for one reason or another. Such chemicals are given the general name of *pesticide*.

chloroethane. Do you see where the abbreviation comes from? *DichloroDiphenyTrichloroethane.*[10] (In the last few years, more and more chemicals with complicated names are getting to be known by initials. The trend is going too far, perhaps, and some chemists are rather sarcastic about what they call "alphabet soup" names.)

You may feel quite satisfied with the initials. Why use the jawbreaker when the initials do just as well?

However, the name tells us something the initials don't. It tells us what the molecule looks like. The long name ends with "ethane" so we can start with the ethane molecule. It is "trichloroethane" so three of the hydrogen atoms of ethane must be replaced by chlorine atoms. (The prefix "tri" comes from a Greek word meaning "three.") The name further says that two other hydrogen atoms are replaced by chlorophenyl groups, which are benzene rings with one hydrogen atom missing and another replaced by a chlorine atom. So there you are.[11]

Do you wonder why it is important to know the formula?

Remember, it is only by knowing the formula that a chemist knows how to manipulate a compound properly. He can't change one substance into another unless he knows the formula; at least he can't do it intelligently. He can work by the hit-and-miss method, but that's very inefficient.

Some useful organic substances are *natural compounds;* that is, they are obtained from the tissues of some living

[10] One of the things that make chemical names look so complicated is the way they are always run together to form one long word. The name for DDT would look better to our eyes if it were written: dichloro-diphenyl-trichloro-ethane. However, until World War I, organic chemistry was almost entirely a German science. In the German language, words are often run together to make one long word and the Germans don't seem to mind at all. English and American chemists picked up the habit, alas, even thought this is not the way of the English tongue. Now it is too late to do anything about it.

[11] Actually, this is not the whole story. Which hydrogen atoms are replaced by chlorine atoms and which by chlorophenyl groups? The full Geneva name of the compound is: 1, 1, 1-trichloro-2, 2-(*bis*-p-chlorophenyl) ethane. A name such as this may look horrible but it describes the chemical formula at a glance to the chemist. With a little practice it would do the same for you.

organism; or from the action of some living organism on its surroundings; or from the remains of some once-living organism. Other organic substances do not exist in nature, but are manufactured by chemists. These are *synthetic compounds*. (The word "synthetic" comes from two Greek words meaning "put together.") DDT is an example of a synthetic compound.

Our daily life now depends on thousands of synthetics. (Think how an insecticide like DDT helps increase our food supply by killing insects that feed on our crops; how it cuts down the death rate from diseases like malaria and typhus which are carried by insects.)

As another example, consider *Saran*. This is a synthetic compound which is seen most often as a thin, transparent film. It is sold in rolls and is used in the kitchen to wrap food, cover dishes, and so on. It is made of long-chain molecules like polyethylene except that every other carbon atom is bonded to either one or two chlorine atoms. Still another example is *Neoprene*, an artificial rubber. This consists of a hydrocarbon chain with a chlorine atom attached to every fourth carbon atom. It is built up from a compound like isoprene but with a chlorine replacing the branched carbon atom. This compound is called *chloroprene*.

Synthetics such as these are built up purposely by chemists who know how to force atoms together in some particular pattern. They must also have a good idea, in advance, of what kind of properties such a pattern is likely to have. This cannot be done without considerable knowledge of the atomic structure of organic molecules.

So it is all very well to use names like DDT or Saran. Most of us don't need to know any more than that. Still, there must always be some people who know the full name that goes with the initials or with the trade-name, and what it means structurally, or all of us will be the worse for it.

Refrigeration and Hospital Smell

It is only rather recently that useful compounds containing fluorine have been developed. The most familiar is *dichlorodifluoromethane*, which is better-known under the trade-name

Freon. As you can tell from the chemical name, the molecule of Freon consists of methane with all four hydrogen atoms replaced, two by chlorine atoms and two by fluorine atoms.

Freon is a *refrigerant*; that is, it can be used to keep things colder than the surrounding temperature. A substance, to be used as a refrigerant, must be a gas which can easily be made liquid by pressure. (Its boiling point must not be too far below 0° C., in other words.)

If such a substance is put through pipes under pressure, so that it is liquid, and the pressure is then removed, the liquid turns into a gas. In so doing, it removes heat from whatever it is in contact with. (This is similar to the way in which evaporating water cools the skin, or evaporating ethyl chloride freezes it.) The gas is liquefied and allowed to evaporate over and over again. Heat is removed and removed and removed (and carried away either by the air or by running water). In this way, the contents of a refrigerator, of a room, or even of a large box-car can be kept well below room temperature, or even well below freezing.

The ordinary liquids used for this purpose are the inorganic compounds, ammonia (boiling point, —33° C.) or sulfur dioxide (boiling point, —10° C.). Both are quite cheap and are still used in large industrial refrigerating equipment. In smaller units, such as home refrigerators, or room air-conditioners, it is Freon that it being used more and more. Its boiling point is —28° C.

Although more expensive than the inorganic refrigerants, Freon has several very important advantages. Ammonia and sulfur dioxide have very irritating and unpleasant odors and are quite poisonous. An accidental leak in the freezing coil would be most unpleasant and could be fatal. Furthermore, both ammonia and sulfur dioxide will corrode many metals. Freon, on the other hand, is odorless, non-poisonous, and non-corrosive. Unlike most organic compounds, it is completely non-inflammable so that we are spared even the danger of fire and explosion.

Organic compounds that contain fluorine show promise for the future. Chlorine, bromine, and iodine are rather large atoms and they sometimes can't replace all the hydrogen atoms in an organic compound. If they try, they get in their own way. Fluorine, however, takes up little room in a molecule. (In fact, the only atom that takes up less room is the hydrogen atom.) For that reason, it can easily replace all the hydrogen atoms. Compounds made up of carbon atoms and fluorine atoms only are called *fluorocarbons*.

Fluorocarbons are much more stable than the hydrocarbons. They are less affected by chemicals or by heat. They won't dissolve in water and will hardly dissolve in anything else. Long fluorocarbon chains can be made into interesting plastics. One such has been prepared by Dupont under the trade-name, *Teflon*. It is also called *Fluon*. It is unaffected by the strongest acids or by heat up to 325° C. It is also an excellent electrical insulator.

Fluorocarbons of different types are now coming into use as artificial rubbers, as lubricants and as fire extinguishers. They are also placed in cans under pressure, so that upon release, they can force out whip cream, shaving soap or any of dozens of other articles.

The most important hydrocarbon containing bromine is *ethylene dibromide*. This is a two-carbon compound with a bromine atom attached to each carbon atom. Ethylene dibromide is added to leaded gasoline to take care of the lead. Ordinarily, the lead atoms in the burning gasoline would settle out in the engine and ruin it. With ethylene bromide around, lead atoms combine with the bromine atoms to form lead bromide. At the temperature of the working engine, lead bromide turns to vapor. It is expelled through the exhaust and the lead atoms are gone.

A compound with a more old-fashioned use is *iodoform*. This is a yellow solid that has a certain ability to kill germs. In other words, it is a mild *antiseptic*. At one time, doctors used iodoform freely to dust on wounds and bandages. Iodoform has a strong odor and hospitals and doctors' offices used to smell strongly of it. It is the "hospital smell" many people remember. Partly because of this odor, iodoform has gone out of fashion. Another reason is that other and better ways of guarding against infection have been discovered.

Chapter 5

Beverages and Poisons

The Use and Abuse of Oxygen

Now IT IS TIME to speak of still another type of atom: the *oxygen atom.*

Oxygen is a gas, with a molecule made up of two oxygen atoms. One-fifth of the atmosphere is oxygen gas. Oxygen is not as active as fluorine or chlorine, but it is active enough to keep us alive; and active enough to be very destructive sometimes.

Oxygen atoms combine with the carbon and hydrogen of organic compounds. They continue to do so until the various carbon and hydrogen atoms are hanging on to as many oxygen atoms as they can. At room temperature the process is very slow; so slow, usually, as to be completely unnoticeable. If the temperature is raised, the process speeds up. At a certain temperature, the *ignition point,* the atoms of the organic compound combine with oxygen atoms so rapidly that the energy released can be seen and felt. The organic compound burns. Whether the process is slow enough to be unnoticeable or fast enough to be a fire or even an explosion, it is called an *oxidation.*

When an organic molecule has been completely oxidized, the carbon atoms are all converted to *carbon dioxide.* Its molecule is made up of one carbon atom and two oxygen atoms. The hydrogen atoms of the organic molecule have been converted to water, with molecules made up of two hydrogen atoms and one oxygen atom.

Oxidation goes on continuously in our body, but in a very slow, gentle and controlled way. The energy released by the oxidation is stored in the form of special compounds. When these special compounds (called "high-energy compounds") are broken up, they release the energy as needed. The released energy is then used to run the body machinery.

When we inhale, we pull oxygen into our lungs. From the lungs, oxygen is absorbed into the bloodstream and carried to all parts of the body. This oxygen combines with the organic compounds which have been obtained from the food that has been eaten, digested, and absorbed. The energy is used and the carbon dioxide that is formed is expelled when we exhale.

If, for any reason, our oxygen supply is shut off for as short a time as five minutes, we die. Our life is extinguished just as a fire in a furnace would be if the oxygen supply were shut off for even a short while.

So you see, life depends on controlled oxidation. The usefulness of a furnace, a gas range, or a match also depends on controlled oxidation.

We are all also acquainted with examples of uncontrolled oxidation that can do much harm—forest fires and gasoline explosions, for instance. All civilized communities support a fire department whose special duty it is to keep houses from burning; or to keep damage to a minimum once burning starts.

What a Difference an O Makes

The chemical symbol for oxygen is just its initial, O. The oxygen atom is capable of forming two bonds. It will hook up with two hydrogen atoms to form water. It will also occupy two of the four bonds of a carbon atom while another oxygen atom will occupy the other two. In this way carbon dioxide is formed.

Suppose, though, that an oxygen atom is attached to a carbon atom with one bond and a hydrogen atom with the other. The atom combination would look like this: C-O-H.

Any molecule that contains such a combination is called an *alcohol*. This word is derived from the Arabic and reminds us that during the early Middle Ages, the Arabs (and the Moslem world generally) were far ahead of Europe in science.

The simplest alcohol is one with a molecule containing only a single carbon atom, thus:

Figure 22—Methyl Alcohol

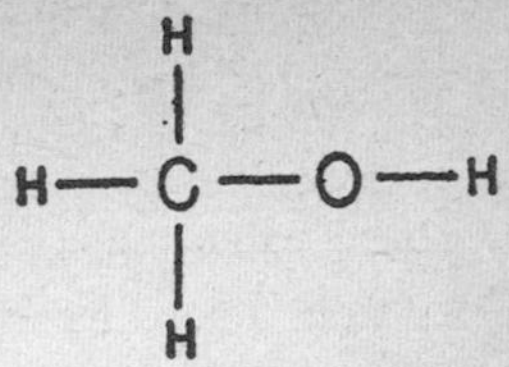

$$H-\overset{\displaystyle H}{\underset{\displaystyle H}{\overset{|}{\underset{|}{C}}}}-O-H$$

Since this contains a methyl group, it is called *methyl alcohol*.

Methyl alcohol differs from methane because one hydrogen atom of methane has been replaced by an oxygen-hydrogen combination. (This O-H combination is called a *hydroxyl group*.) What a difference that extra oxygen atom makes!

A hydroxyl group in a molecule gives that molecule electrical properties resembling those of water. This means that whereas methane will not dissolve in water, methyl alcohol will. In fact, any amount of methyl alcohol will mix freely with any amount of water so that you could never tell from looking at the mixture that there were two different liquids to begin with. Methyl alcohol and water are, for that reason, said to be *miscible in all proportions*.

A hydroxyl group also makes a difference in the boiling point of a compound. The electrical properties of a hydroxyl group are such that molecules containing them stick together slightly. The molecules of liquid methane, which contain no hydroxyl groups, don't stick together. They are easy to pull apart into a vapor. Even at the frigid temperature of —161° C. there is enough heat present to supply the energy to vaporize methane. Therefore, —161° C. is the boiling point of methane. Each molecule of methyl alcohol, however, has a hydroxyl group which makes it "sticky." To pull those molecules apart and make a vapor out of them takes considerable energy, even though the molecules aren't much larger than those of methane. That is why the boiling point of methyl alcohol is 65° C.—226 degrees higher than the boiling point of methane.

Two hydroxyl groups sticking together form a *hydrogen bond*. It can be written this way —O—H . . . O—H—, with the dotted line representing the hydrogen bond. (Certain other atom combinations can also stick together in this way.) The hydrogen bond is only 5 percent as strong as ordinary bonds between atoms but they are terribly important. The enormous molecules of some of the complicated substances in our bodies are kept from falling apart by the hydrogen bonds that hold different parts of the molecule together.

An early method of preparing methyl alcohol was to heat wood in the absence of air. The complicated molecules in the wood broke up into smaller molecules as a result of the heat. These smaller molecules were given off in the form of vapors. These vapors did not burn since air was absent. They were collected and liquefied and a number of substances, including methyl alcohol, were obtained in this way. Because of this, the common name for methyl alcohol is *wood alcohol*.

The word "methyl" also goes back to that same process. It comes from Greek words meaning "wood wine." Since "methyl" applies to the alcohol with one carbon atom in its molecule, chemists decided to give the name "methane" to the hydrocarbon with one carbon atom in its molecule.[1]

Methyl alcohol is important in industry as a starting point for the manufacture of more complicated molecules. It also has another use, which needs some explaining.

Solid materials react very slowly. When chemists work with these solids they usually want to speed up the reactions. This is particularly true in industrial plants where tons of material may be involved. In order to speed things up, the solid material is dissolved in a liquid. Then, in solution, it can react very quickly.

The trick is to find a liquid that will dissolve the particular solid materials involved; to find a proper *solvent,* in other words. Many solids will dissolve in water and water is the most important solvent we have. However, many organic solids will not dissolve in water, but will dissolve in certain

---

[1] The official Geneva name for methyl alcohol is *methanol*. The suffix "ol" is given to all alcohols. Other types of compounds should not be given that suffix. Sometimes the aromatic hydrocarbons—benzine, toluene, and xylene—are called "benzol," "toluol," and "xylol." This is a bad habit picked up from the Germans and is frowned upon by American chemists.

organic liquids. Therefore, these organic liquids are also important solvents.

To be really useful, solvents must be abundant and cheap. They must have a fairly low boiling point so that they can be easily vaporized away when they are no longer needed.

Methyl alcohol, with its boiling point of 65° C., is an example of an excellent industrial solvent. Another important industrial solvent, by the way, is benzene, and there are many others as well. Each different solvent has its own particular value. Some solids, you see, may dissolve in one but not in another; a particular reaction may go well in one but not in another. The industrial chemist working with his tons of chemicals must be as particular in his ingredients as the master chef preparing a wedding cake.

The Cup that Cheers

The most famous alcohol of all is the two-carbon variety. Its formula looks like this:

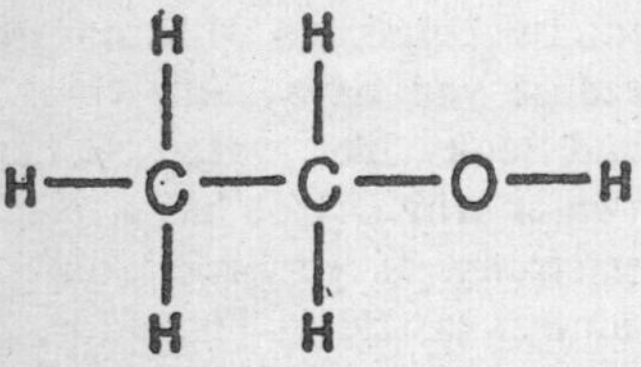

Figure 23—Ethyl Alcohol

Since this compound contains the ethyl group, it is called *ethyl alcohol*. Its official Geneva name is *ethanol*.

Ethyl alcohol is so important that when people (even chemists) say just "alcohol," they always mean "ethyl alcohol" and not any of the trillions of other possible alcohols.

It is difficult to know just what to say about ethyl alcohol. To the chemist, it is a particularly important compound. It is useful in many chemical reactions and, at the same time, quite cheap.[2] It is often important to the layman, too, but for him, it does not always serve a useful purpose.

[2] Ethyl alcohol is cheap, that is, if it is being used for scientific work. When it is used for other purposes, it is usually severely

Man learned about ethyl alcohol thousands of years ago, before civilization had its beginnings. There is no mystery as to how that came about. If fruits, or fruit juices, are allowed to stand about in the open, microscopic living cells (always present in the atmosphere) will fall in. Some will grow in the juice, living on the sugar it contains. The cells change the sugar into ethyl alcohol, using the energy freed by this chemical change for their growth and multiplication.

Fruit juices that are affected in this way are said to be *fermented*. Primitive man, drinking juice that had accidentally fermented, must have liked the taste or the way it made him feel. At least, it is pretty certain that he began to allow fruit juice to ferment on purpose. The earliest civilizations we know already had regular methods for producing fermented drinks.

Fermented fruit-juice, particularly fermented grape-juice, is called wine. Even the Bible shows how ancient the practice seemed even to the ancients, themselves. *Genesis* 9: 20-21 describes how Noah, after the flood, first cultivated the grape-vine and prepared wine. (It also describes the bad effects.)

You mustn't think that you are acquainted with the properties of ethyl alcohol just because you have seen wine. Pure ethyl alcohol is colorless and looks like water. (Chemists sometimes describe this as "water white.") It has a pleasant, sweetish smell, but not very strong. If you mix some with water, the mixture will be almost tasteless. The odor, taste, and color of wines is due not to ethyl alcohol but to other compounds. That is why there are so many different kinds of wine. The taste varies according to the particular juices used to begin with and the particular method by which it is allowed to ferment.

Starchy foods, like the grains, will also ferment, and ethyl alcohol will be produced from the starch. Grains which are allowed to sprout in moist heat (such sprouted grain is called malt) produce beer and ale. Such drinks were so popular and inexpensive in many parts of the world that the common name

taxed. Most chemical laboratories keep their supply of ethyl alcohol locked away, to make sure it is used for scientific work only.

for ethyl alcohol is *grain alcohol*. One of the most popular grains for the purpose was barley. A grain of barley is called a barleycorn. ("Corn" is really an old-fashioned word for "kernel.") Consequently, alcoholic drinks today are sometimes referred to jokingly as "Old John Barleycorn."

Alcoholic drinks in moderation are found by many people to have a pleasant effect. They are stimulating, warming, seem to make one's self and other people friendlier and happier and so on. However, in greater amounts, they confuse a person's muscular co-ordination, upset his judgment, cause him to do foolish and even harmful things, and make him feel ill for a period of time.

Both the pleasant and the harmful effects can be strengthened by increasing the alcoholic content of the beverage. Ordinary beers and wines can't be more than about 15 percent alcohol. By the time the alcohol builds up to that amount, it kills the living cells that are doing the fermenting. Fermentation comes to a halt.

Man learned how to get around that, however. The boiling point of ethyl alcohol is 78° C., which is lower than that of water. If beer or wine is heated, the alcohol in the beverage evaporates and boils more quickly than the water does. The vapors that come off are richer in alcohol than the original liquor was. If these vapors are trapped and allowed to cool into a liquid again, you have a stronger drink (that is, one with more ethyl alcohol) than you started with.

This process of turning liquid into vapor, then back to liquid, is known as *distillation*. (I spoke of fractional distillation, you may remember, when I discussed petroleum refining.) The stronger alcoholic beverages are therefore called *distilled liquors*, and the equipment used to prepare them are called *stills*. By distillation, wine can be converted into brandy; beer can be converted into whiskey.

A word you may have heard in connection with whiskey is "proof." The proof of an alcoholic drink is a number equal to twice the percent of alcohol present. If a wine contains 18 percent alcohol, it is 36 proof. If a whiskey contains 50 percent alcohol, it is 100 proof.

In the chemistry laboratory, ethyl alcohol is usually used

95 percent pure (190 proof). The last 5 percent of water is hard to get rid of. When it is removed, *absolute alcohol* (100 percent or 200 proof) is obtained. This is quite expensive and must be handled carefully. The least exposure to air will result in its absorbing water vapor from the air and then it will no longer be "absolute."

Ethyl alcohol is a mild antiseptic. For this purpose, a 70 percent solution of alcohol in water (140 proof) is used. Generally, when a doctor or nurse is about to give you an injection, the spot where the hypodermic needle is to enter is first swabbed with a wad of cotton soaked in 70 percent alcohol. This kills skin bacteria which might otherwise enter with the needle and infect you.

Ethyl alcohol will burn. It already has some oxygen in its molecule so it produces only three-fourths of the energy that hydrocarbon will produce when it burns. Ethyl alcohol is also more expensive than gasoline. Still, when the day comes that the oil wells begin to fail us, we may find that our automobiles will have to run on alcohol.

The early chemists who first dealt with liquids that evaporated easily (as ethyl alcohol does) did not quite know what to make of it. They didn't have the equipment to handle vapors. It seemed to them that liquids just vanished when they evaporated. The very word "gas" when it was first invented was taken from the word "chaos" which shows how mysterious the whole thing seemed.

There was something ghost-like and insubstantial about gases to these early chemists. They called liquids that turned into gases easily, "spirits." Methyl alcohol, they called "wood spirit"; ethyl alcohol, "wine spirit." Even today, alcoholic beverages are frequently referred to as "spirits." (Modern Arabs, from whose language the word "alcohol" was taken, call ethyl alcohol "spirit" from the English. This is a queer interchange.)

The Cup that Kills

Ethyl alcohol may be harmful when taken in excess, but the other liquid alcohols are all worse. As little as a third of an ounce of methyl alcohol, for instance, will cause permanent blindness.

For a period of thirteen years, from 1920 to 1933, the United States tried to avoid some of the evils of alcohol intoxication by prohibiting the sale of beverages containing more than 0.5 percent of ethyl alcohol. (This was known as "Prohibition.") The experiment failed because alcoholic drinks were sold illegally in great quantities. Furthermore, a great deal of poor-grade liquor was manufactured in home stills. Sometimes unscrupulous people would add methyl alcohol to the final results, since methyl alcohol could be bought legally and fairly cheaply and it made the liquor "stronger." It also made the liquor poisonous. A shocking number of deaths were brought about by such poison liquor.

Ethyl alcohol can be made poisonous. When ethyl alcohol is used in industry (as a solvent, for instance), poisonous and foul-tasting substances are deliberately added to it. This is done to keep people from drinking it and to avoid increased costs. Drinkable alcohol, you see, is highly taxed, but undrinkable alcohol (called *denatured alcohol*) is not.

Denatured alcohol is sometimes used in automobiles. Ethyl alcohol has a very low freezing point, —117° C. The freezing point of water is 0° C. These two facts become important to the car-owner in the winter. Water is used in the car's radiator to keep the engine from getting too hot as it works. The engine uses up its heat in warming the water which is then circulated through the radiator so that it gives up its heat to the air.

This is all very well, but comes the winter and a cold snap. The car, standing in the street or in an unheated garage, gets cold. The water in the radiator freezes, expands, and cracks the radiator block. Expensive damage is done. For that reason, when winter aproaches, the motorist adds a liquid to the water in the radiator to lower its freezing point. The added liquid is an *anti-freeze*. Denatured alcohol is often used as an anti-freeze. Add enough and no winter day will be bad enough to freeze your car. Methyl alcohol can also be used for this purpose.

However, while the engine is working, even on a cold day, the alcohol water mixture gets quite warm and slowly the alcohol evaporates away. If there is a warm snap, it evaporates away that much faster. For this reason, methyl or ethyl alcohol are only temporary anti-freeze compounds and more must be added every once in a while.

Alcohol solutions are often used externally as in *rubbing alcohol* for its effect in toning up the skin and soothing muscular aches. For similar reasons, it is used in hair lotions, after shaving lotions, and so on.

Manufacturers don't like to use ethyl alcohol for the purpose, and they can't use methyl alcohol or denatured alcohol. Instead, they use *isopropyl alcohol*. This is a 3-carbon compound, with the hydroxyl group on the middle carbon. Its action is very similar to ethyl alcohol. It is more poisonous if taken internally than ethyl alcohol is, but it has a harsher taste so people aren't likely to enjoy drinking it. And at least it is not as poisonous as methyl alcohol.

Isopropyl alcohol is sometimes added to gasoline in the winter. There is always a small amount of water in the gasoline, and ordinarily this causes no trouble. During cold snaps, however, the water will freeze into particles of ice. These may clog the fuel lines and stall the car. If a small quantity of isopropyl alcohol is put into the gas tank, it will mix with the water droplets and keep them from freezing. It is also used in de-icing mixtures intended to get ice off automobile windshields.

The Alcohol Properties Vanish

The alcohols with small molecules, such as methyl, ethyl, and isopropyl alcohols, are all miscible with water in all proportions. This is because of the influence of the hydroxyl group. However, in the molecules of alcohols with long carbon chains, the effect of the hydroxyl group is drowned out. The properties of the carbon chain take over.

Butyl alcohol, for instance, is made up of a four-carbon chain with a hydroxyl group attached. If ten ounces of butyl alcohol are added to ten ounces of water, the two liquids will not mix completely. One ounce of the butyl alcohol will dissolve in the water. A similar small quantity of water will dissolve in the butyl alcohol. The main body of the two liquids will remain apart. There will be a definite line of division (a *phase boundary*) between them. If you shake a bottle containing the two liquids, they will mix temporarily, forming bubbles. As the mixture stands, the two liquids separate and form two layers. The butyl alcohol will be on top because it is lighter than water.

Alcohols with still longer carbon chains are even less soluble in water.

The five-carbon alcohols[3] are known as the *amyl alcohols*. They occur in alcoholic beverages and may be responsible for some of the worse effects of alcoholic overindulgence, the so-called "hangover." This longer-chain alcohol portion of the beverage is sometimes referred to as *fusel oil*. (The word "fusel" comes from Greek words meaning "inferior spirits.")

---

[3] I refer to them in the plural because they occur as a number of isomers. The hydroxyl group can be in various positions on the chain and the chain itself can be branched in several ways.

Chapter 6

Here and There with the Hydroxyl Group

Vitamins and Eyes

HYDROXYL GROUPS can be attached to any kind of carbon chains or rings and an interesting variety of compounds occurs. There are terpene alcohols, for instance, in which a hydroxyl group is attached to the molecule of a terpene hydrocarbon.

An example is the ten-carbon compound, *menthol,* which occurs in peppermint oils. (In fact, its name comes from the Latin word for "mint.") If menthol is applied to the skin it creates a refreshing, cooling sensation. If it is dissolved in liquid petrolatum and sprayed into the nose or throat, it has a soothing effect on inflamed membranes. It is used in some cough drops and even some cigarettes, for that reason.

For a more important compound, let's go back to carotene. Carotene, you may remember, is a 40-carbon compound, built up out of eight isoprene units and containing a number of double bonds. Well, one of those double bonds is right in the middle of the chain.

Now the body can break the carotene molecule at that middle double bond. In the most common variety of carotene the two "half-molecules" formed in this way are identical. At the broken end of each "half-molecule" a hydroxyl group is formed. In place of the original 40-carbon carotene, there are now two 20-carbon alcohols.

This 20-carbon alcohol, built up out of four isoprene units, is *vitamin A*. Since the body can form vitamin A from carotene, carotene is sometimes called *provitamin A*. (The prefix "pro" in both Latin and Greek means "before.")

The human body makes use of vitamin A (or of compounds very like it) in the retina of the eye particularly, to help us see in dim light. Only small quantities are necessary for that purpose, but even these small quantities pose a problem. The body can't manufacture vitamin A out of simpler substances, the way it can most of the compounds in its tissues.[1] It can only make it out of carotene, and it can't make carotene out of any simpler substance, either. This means that the human diet must contain small quantities of either vitamin A or carotene or we will be in trouble. Foods such as milk, butter, and eggs contain vitamin A. Carrots, tomatoes, and some other vegetables contain carotene.

The body stores vitamin A in the liver if more is taken in than is required for immediate use. Then, if the diet is short in vitamin A for a time, the body uses what it has previously stored. If the storage continues, however, we do run out eventually. When we do, the human eye can no longer function as it should in dim light. The condition that results is known as *night blindness*. The moist membranes in the nose and throat, and particularly around the eye, become dry and scaly. This condition is known as *xerophthalmia,* from Greek words meaning "dry eyes." For this reason, the official chemical name for vitamin A is *axerophthol* (meaning "no dry eyes").

Vitamins and Bones

There is another alcohol that is a vitamin and this involves the steroid nucleus mentioned in Chapter 3. The most common steroid in the body is one which contains one double bond, three hydrocarbon side-chains at various points, and a hydroxyl group. I won't give the details of the formula, but here is the diagram of the steroid nucleus again so you can see exactly where the hydroxyl group is attached, where the double bond is, and where the side-chains are:

[1] There are a number of organic compounds which the body must have, for life and health, in small quantities, which it cannot make for itself. Over a dozen different kinds, in fact. These are the *vitamins,* and vitamin A is only one of them.

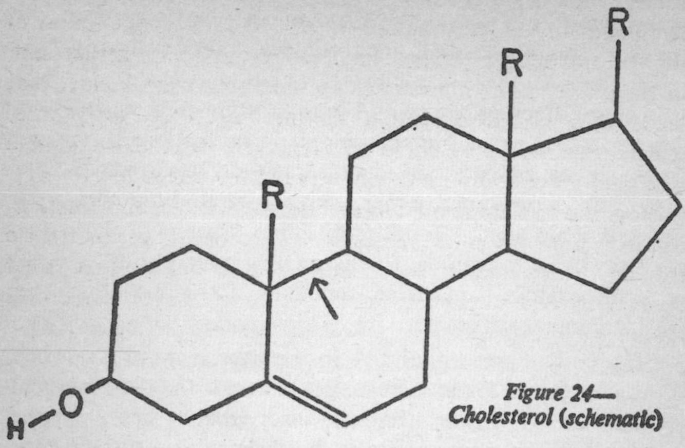

Figure 24—
Cholesterol (schematic)

The R stands for the hydrocarbon side-chains.[2] The arrow will be explained later.

Any steroid that contains a hydroxyl group is called a *sterol*. This word comes from a Greek word meaning "solid" because the sterols were the earliest (or one of the earliest) known alcohols that happened to be solid at room temperature. Once the chemical structure was worked out, then other compounds with similar structure but without the hydroxyl group were given the name "steroid" meaning "sterol-like." (The suffix "oid" comes from the Greek and means "similar to.")

The particular sterol that is common in the body and has the formula shown above is *cholesterol*. The prefix "chole" comes from the Greek word for "liver bile." This is a digestive fluid manufactured by the liver and poured into the intestine.

The name is a good one, because the liver bile happens to contain a good deal of cholesterol. In fact, it contains more than is good for us sometimes. The bile is stored in the gall bladder and becomes particularly thick and concentrated

---

[2] Sometimes the organic chemist wants to show that there is a carbon chain or ring attached to a certain spot in a molecule but finds the details of the chain unimportant at the moment. When that happens, he saves time by just writing R to represent the group.

there. Cholesterol is not very soluble and if enough of it accumulates in the gall bladder, it will come out of solution in the form of little crystals. The crystals may join together and, in time, may grow big enough to block the narrow duct that leads from the gall bladder to the intestine. These *gall stones*, which are almost pure cholesterol, can give rise to considerable pain and an operation may be required for relief.

You mustn't think of cholesterol as just a trouble-maker, though. Only a small number of people have gall-stone trouble. Every human being, on the other hand, has a great deal of cholesterol in the brain and nervous system. Almost half the solid matter in the brain is cholesterol. It forms an important part of the insulating myelin sheaths about the nerves. It is also used by the body to manufacture vital chemicals that are needed in small amounts.

Sterols and sunshine make an interesting combination. When exposed to the ultra-violet rays of the sun, one of the rings of the steroid nucleus breaks. The bond that breaks is the one to which I have pointed an arrow in the cholesterol formula. When this happens to certain sterols (not all), molecules of *vitamin D* result.

Now the body can make its own sterols, but it can't break the bond that must be broken to form vitamin D. That's why children must have vitamin D in their diet, as well as getting a certain amount of sunlight. It is for this reason that vitamin D is sometimes called the "sunshine vitamin." It isn't in sunshine, of course, but sunshine helps produce it out of sterols that are in the skin.

Vitamin D helps in the proper formation of bones, in growing children. Since the chief element in bone is calcium, vitamin D has been named *calcifero*[8] from Greek words meaning "calcium carrying." Youngsters who are deficient in vitamin D can develop soft bones which are easily bent or deformed and which then remain that way permanently. This condition

---

[8] Vitamins were discovered by means of nutritional experiments years before chemists had worked out their structure. For that reason, they were called by letters of the alphabet. Once the structures were worked out, they were given actual names. On the whole, chemists consider it better practice to use the names rather than the letters.

is known as *rickets*. It is more likely to happen among children who are born in the winter or in northern latitudes because it is then that sunlight is particularly weak and least likely to form the vitamin D.

Rickets, xerophthalmia, and other *vitamin deficiency diseases* are much less common in the civilized world (particularly in the United States) than they used to be. First, scientists discovered that vitamins existed and learned the foods in which they were to be found. In this way, a healthful diet could be worked out. Secondly, chemists learned the structure of vitamins and learned how to make some synthetically.[4] The result is that a large quantity of vitamin pills and concentrates are for sale on the counters of any drug store. Probably every reader of this book has taken vitamin pills at one time or another. Here is another example of the way knowledge of structural formulas has helped the health of mankind.

However, it should not be assumed that because a little of something is good, a lot of it is better. The two vitamins we have just discussed, vitamin A and vitamin D, can actually harm the body if taken in too great a quantity. (Disorders caused by too many vitamins are called *hypervitaminoses*.) In these days of vitamin pills (especially for children with over-enthusiastic mothers) there is actually more danger of people taking too much vitamin preparation than too little.

Sweetness

Must we confine ourselves to one hydroxyl group per molecule? Chemists, indeed, have found it impossible (except in rare cases) to put more than one hydroxyl group on a single carbon atom. Such an arrangement is unstable. The atoms rearrange themselves at once into more stable combinations. However, you can have a hydroxyl group on different carbon atoms in a molecule. You can even have one on every carbon atom in a molecule.

[4] You mustn't suppose that a synthetic substance is inferior to a natural substance, or just a kind of substitute. If the structure of a molecule is known and that molecule is made in the laboratory, the product is identical with the natural one. The only difference is the place of manufacture; the laboratory instead of living tissue.

The simplest case of this is a two-carbon compound with two hydroxyl groups:

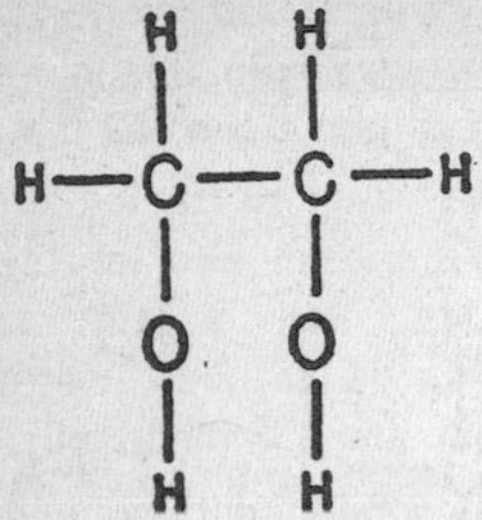

Figure 25—Ethylene Glycol

This compound is *ethylene glycol*. Any compound with two hydroxyl groups on adjacent carbon atoms is called a glycol, but when the word "glycol" is used all by itself, it is generally intended to mean ethylene glycol.

The presence of a number of hydroxyl groups in a compound makes a molecule more soluble in water and gives it a higher boiling point than similar compounds with fewer hydroxyl groups. It also often causes a compound (for no reason we know) to be sweet-tasting. For instance, ethylene glycol tastes as sweet as sugar. The very name "glycol" comes from a Greek work meaning "sweet."

The most important use of ethylene glycol has nothing to do with its sweetness. Ethylene glycol freezes at —17° C. Water, as I've said several times, freezes at 0° C. Now it is almost always true that a mixture of two substances will freeze at a lower temperature than either substance separately. If six parts of ethylene glycol are mixed with four parts of water, the mixture doesn't freeze till a temperature of —49° C. is reached.

I've already mentioned the use of denatured ethyl alcohol as an anti-freeze. Well, adding ethylene glycol to the water in an automobile radiator will also prevent it from freezing in the winter. There is an important difference, though, in favor of the ethylene glycol.

Ethyl alcohol boils at 78° C. but ethylene glycol boils at 197° C. When the liquid in a car's radiator warms up as the engine works, it gets warm enough to evaporate the ethyl alcohol but it never gets warm enough to evaporate much of the ethylene glycol. What little evaporation there is, takes place very slowly. Ethylene glycol is a *permanent anti-freeze*.

An even more important *polyhydroxyl compound* (that is, one with many hydroxyl groups) is *glycerol*. This is a three-carbon compound with a hydroxyl group on each carbon atom:

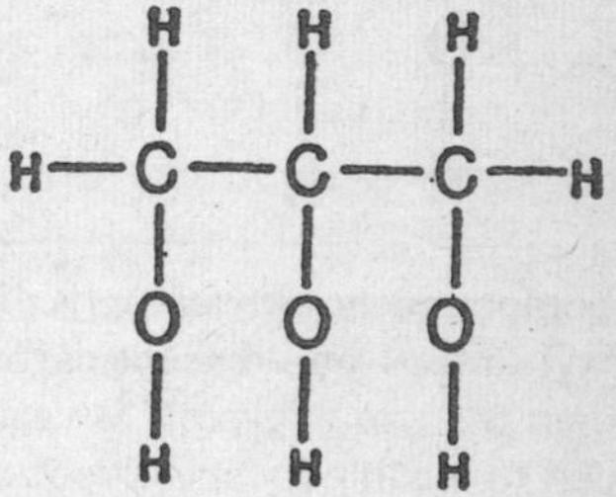

Figure 26—Glycerol

(Sometimes the compound is called "glycerine" but chemists prefer to keep the "ol" suffix.)

The name glycerol also comes from the Greek word meaning "sweet" and glycerol is, in fact, sweet, just as glycol is. Glycol is rather poisonous, but glycerol is completely harmless to the body. You can eat al the glycerol you want. Sometimes you do, in fact. Glycerol is added to cream-centered candies to increase the smoothness of the cream without taking away any of its sweetness. It also prevents the cream from drying out. It doesn't evaporate itself (its boiling point is far too high for it to evaporate at room temperature) and it holds on to water tightly and keeps it from evaporating also.

Because of this "keep-moist" property of glycerol (which chemists refer to as *hygroscopic*), it may be added to tobacco. It keeps the tobacco from drying out and allows it to burn evenly and slowly. Glycerol is also found in lotions used for rough or chapped skin.

As far as the human body is concerned, the most important thing about glycerol is that its molecule combines with other substances to make up the fats and oils of living organisms.

Important in a similar way is a six-carbon ring with a hydroxyl group attached to each of the six carbon atoms, and with no double bonds present. This compound is called *inositol*. It makes up part of the molecules of certain complicated substances found mostly in brain and nerves.

First Victory Over Infection

Before doctors were aware of the existence of germs, any kind of serious wound or surgery was likely to be fatal. Even if the patient could endure the pain (there were no anesthetics, you know) and survived the bleeding and the shock, bacterial infection would set in to finish the job.

In the middle 1800s, the French chemist Louis Pasteur first advanced the germ theory of disease. He proclaimed, and proved, that disease and infections were caused by microscopic organisms.[5] To prevent infection, then, it is necessary to kill these tiny creatures. (Incidentally it is interesting to note that the germ theory of disease, which is the greatest single advance ever made in medicine, was not the work of a physician, but of a chemist.)

In 1865, a Scottish surgeon, Joseph Lister, found a practical way to kill germs. He used chemicals. While treating a patient with a compound fracture of a bone (that is, a fracture where the bone had broken through the skin), he applied a chemical known as *phenol* to the wound. (A solution of one ounce of phenol in three quarts of water will kill most bacteria in five minutes.) He continued to apply it daily and the patient recovered without infection.

This was the beginning. Phenol itself turned out to be too

---

[5] "Germ" is the name given to any tiny object bearing life. A seed, for instance, is a kind of germ. The embryo plant of a wheat seed is called "wheat-germ." Disease can be caused by a variety of germs. Some diseases are caused by bacteria which are microscopic one-celled plants, or fungi, which are somewhat more complicated plants. (Often, bacteria are classified among the fungi.) Disease can also be caused by protozoa, which are microscopic one-celled animals, or by viruses, which are too small to be seen at all by ordinary microscopes, and which are neither plants nor animals. Nowadays, all these creatures are referred to as *microorganisms*.

irritating and damaging to tissues to use generally. It was mixed with other substances. Other chemicals which would kill germs even more easily and damage the patient less were discovered. Even so, the strength of the newer antiseptics is still measured as the *phenol coefficient;* that is, as how much stronger than phenol the particular antiseptic is.

Lister was the originator of antiseptic surgery. Nowadays, doctors wash their hands and arms thoroughly before operations, wear masks, and sterilize their instruments before using them. Germs just aren't given a chance.

The molecule of phenol is made up of a benzene ring to which a hydroxyl group is attached, thus:

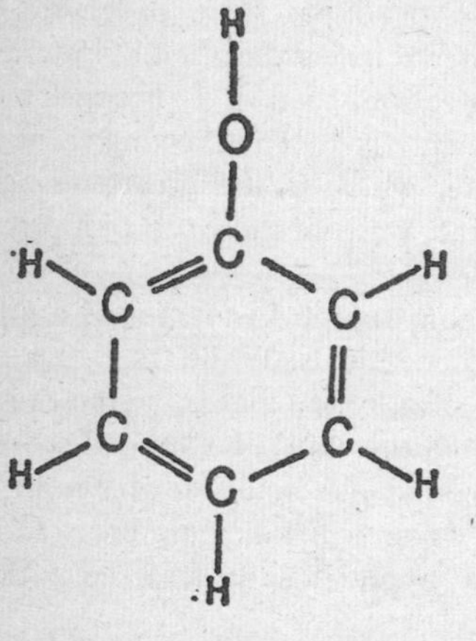

Figure 27—Phenol

Generally, any compound containing a hydroxyl group attached to a benzene ring is called a phenol, but the name is applied particularly to the compound shown in the formula.

Phenol was discovered in 1834 in coal-tar. At that time, coal-tar was used mostly to produce illuminating gas, and the prefix "phen" comes from a Greek word meaning "to illuminate."

An example of a more complicated phenol is *urushiol,* in which there are two hydroxyl groups attached to the benzene ring, as well as a 15-carbon chain. Some of you may have come in contact with urushiol and, if so, you have surely regretted it, because urushiol is the poison in poison ivy.

Acids and Hormones

Phenol is sometimes called *carbolic acid*. In order to explain that, I must first explain what an acid is. Certain compounds occasionally lose part of a hydrogen atom that ordinarily forms part of their molecules. They don't lose a whole hydrogen atom, but just a part of it. The part lost is called a *hydrogen ion.*[6]

Compounds that allow hydrogen ions to break away from their molecules are *acids*. If the hydrogen ions come off the compound very easily so that a lot of them are present at one time, the compound is a *strong acid*. If the hydrogen ions come off with difficulty so that only a few of them are present at any one time, the compound is a *weak acid*. The hydrogen ion has a sour taste and is very active. It will attack and corrode metals of various kinds. Strong acids are therefore dangerous. Chemists handling them must do so carefully to avoid damaging not only chemical equipment, but clothes, skin, or eyes.

When a hydrogen atom it attached to a carbon atom, there is practically no chance at all of a hydrogen ion breaking loose. When a hydrogen atom is attached to an oxygen atom, as in a hydroxyl group, there is a slight chance of a hydrogen ion breaking loose. Ethyl alcohol is therefore an extremely

---

[6] An atom is made up of a small nucleus in its center (which contains a number of particles bunched together) and anywhere from one to a hundred other particles, called electrons, distributed throughout the rest of the atom. Sometimes an atom (or group of atoms) splits away from a molecule leaving one or more electrons behind. The atoms are then, of course, short those electrons. The rest of the molecule has one or more extra electrons. Atoms or groups of atoms with missing electrons or with extra electrons are called *ions*. Ions have properties that may be quite different from those of the original atom. For instance, the sodium atom and the chlorine atom are both dangerous to life. The sodium ion (one electron missing) and the chloride ion (one electron extra) are not only harmless, but essential to life.

weak acid; so weak, in fact, that only chemists can detect its acidity.

When the hydroxyl group is attached to the benzene ring, however, the chance of a hydrogen ion breaking off is increased to the point where the acid properties are noticeable; still very weak, but noticeable. And that is why phenol is sometimes called carbolic acid.

A compound similar to phenol is *cresol*. This is phenol with a methyl group also present on the benzene ring. It is a stronger antiseptic than phenol, cheaper and easier to handle. Household antiseptic cleaners, such as Lysol, contain cresol or similar compounds. It is the cresol that gives them their odor.[7]

Tannins are plant products with rather complicated molecules. These contain two or more benzene rings, each with two hydroxyls attached. They are, therefore, *polyphenols*. The tannins combine with substances in the skin and hide of animals, hardening and toughening them. Hides, treated with tannins, are "tanned" and are converted to leather.

Tannins will also harden skin which has been burned and lessen the pain of the burn. That is why tea-leaves (which contain tannins) are sometimes soaked and placed over a burn. (Incidentally, milk or cream added to coffee or tea combines with some of the tannins soaked out of the tea-leaves or coffee-beans. It is the tannins that give those beverages some of their bitter taste and milk or cream makes them less bitter, for that reason.)

An interesting phenol with medical importance is *diethylstilbestrol*, also called simply *stilbestrol*. Its molecule contains two phenol groups connected by a two-carbon bridge.[8] Stilbestrol is an example of a substitute hormone.

[7] The most common household antiseptic is, of course, tincture of iodine. Lately, a "colorless iodine" has been put on the market. It can be put on cuts without leaving brown splotches on the skin. This is not really iodine but an *iodo-alcohol* (that is, a compound containing both iodine atoms and hydroxyl groups). "Colorless iodine" has a molecule made up of three carbon atoms, with a hydroxyl group attached to one and iodine atoms attached to each of the other two.

[8] I will occasionally talk about "bridges" connecting rings. That's the easiest way to describe that particular situation without drawing formulas, and I am trying to keep the formulas in this book

Hormones are chemicals that are produced in the body by certain small organs called *ductless glands*. These are discharged into the blood in very small quantities and have a powerful effect on the chemical machinery of particular parts of the body. It is as a result of hormone activity, for instance, that a boy or girl changes into a man or woman at adolescence.

Hormones are sometimes used by doctors to help relieve a patient of some disorder. To get enough of certain hormones out of the small quantities present in domestic animals is a long, tedious process. The doctor ends with very little and that very little is very expensive.

However, it is possible to manufacture some of the hormones synthetically in the laboratory. It is even possible, sometimes, to manufacture some other compound, with a molecule easier to put together than that of the hormone, which will have the same effect as the hormone. Stilbestrol is the most successful example. It was first introduced in Europe in 1939 as a substitute for female sex hormones. It is easier to synthesize than female sex hormones, and, in some ways, it actually works better.

---

to a minimum. Two rings connected by a two-carbon bridge would look like this: ring-C-C-ring. A one-carbon bridge would be ring-C-ring. Two rings may even be connected at one corner, and that could be written ring-ring. This is not the same as a fused ring where the two rings are not connected at one corner but along one side. If you have trouble following this, I'm rather glad. It may help convince you that formulas are sometimes easier to understand than words.

Chapter 7

Varying the Combination

—And Still Champion

So FAR, the oxygen atoms in the organic compounds I have mentioned have always been part of hydroxyl groups. Let's change things a bit. Suppose both bonds of the oxygen atom were to be connected to carbon atoms. The combination would look like this: — C — O — C — . Any compound that contains this combination is an *ether*.

The most familiar ether is *diethyl ether*, with a molecule that looks like this:

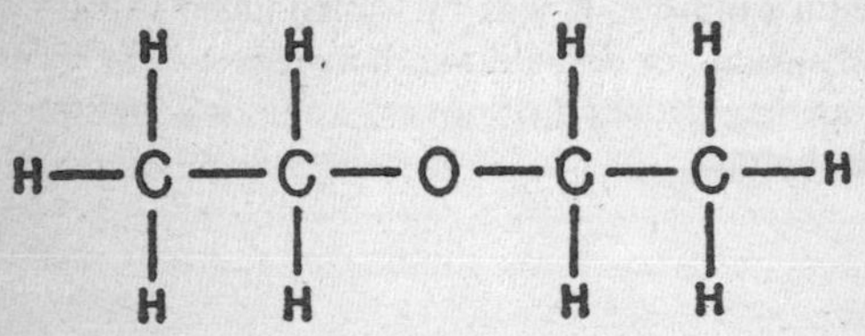

Figure 28— Diethyl Ether

The carbon atoms to which the oxygen atom is attached both belong to ethyl groups; hence the "diethyl" part of the name. Although there are many, many ethers, a chemist or doctor (or anyone else) who says simply "ether" always means diethyl ether.

Diethyl ether was discovered in 1544. At that time virtually nothing was known about organic chemistry. The thing that first amazed the early chemists was that any liquid should evaporate so easily and quickly. The boiling point of diethyl ether is only 34° C. (95° F.)—less than normal body temperature.

As I said earlier in the book, gases and vapors completely mystified the early chemists. To them, this new liquid just seemed to disappear into thin air. The Greeks had a word for the upper regions of the air, high above the lower atmosphere and its earthly corruptions. They called it "aether." In 1730, this vanishing compound which seemed to flee the earth was given the name "spiritus aethereus" (which, in English, means "ethereal spirit"). Eventually, this was shortened to "ether."

Furthermore, the two-carbon groups that were found to form part of the molecule (once chemists learned about atoms and molecules, that is) got their name "ethyl" from the same source. From that came the word "ethane" for the two-carbon hydrocarbon. It frequently happens in organic chemistry that one thing names another in chain fashion.

In some ways ethers have properties part way between alcohols and hydrocarbons, but they are considerably closer to the hydrocarbon. Diethyl ether is slightly soluble in water, but will mix much more easily with fatty substances, including the myelin sheaths of nerve cells.

That makes ether an anesthetic and, in fact, it is a good one. It was one of the first anesthetics used, and is completely American in its origin. In 1842, a Georgia doctor, Crawford Long, operated on a patient under ether. On September 30, 1846, a Boston dentist, W. T. G. Morton extracted a tooth from a patient under ether. Two weeks later, on October 16, 1846, Dr. J. C. Warren performed the first public operation on a patient under ether. That took place at the Massachusetts General Hospital, in Boston.

It was shortly after that that the term "anesthesia" was suggested by Oliver Wendell Holmes, the Boston doctor and poet, best known for his poems *Old Ironsides* and *The Wonderful One-Hoss Shay*.

For over a century, doctors have been experimenting with new anesthetics, and still diethyl ether is used more frequently than any other, particularly for long-drawn-out operations. It is still the champion. Other anesthetics may act more quickly, but diethyl ether is in some ways the safest; it is not as likely to affect heart and lung action as some other anesthetics.

Like most anesthetics except chloroform, diethyl ether is a fire and explosion hazard. Furthermore, if it is allowed to stand, it adds additional oxygen atoms to its molecule to form unstable compounds which can explode even if left undisturbed.

To prevent this, ether intended for anesthetic purposes is carefully purified and stored in small, sealed cans. A piece of iron wire is also included in the can because iron slows down the formation of the explosive compound. Even so, once a can of ether has been open for longer than 24 hours, it is not used for anesthesia.

Diethyl ether has a strong smell which, in small quantities, is not unpleasant. Now that iodoform is no longer used, ether is the most familiar "hospital smell."

Because diethyl ether will dissolve fatty substances very easily, it is useful to chemists. They add it to a mixture of substances and let the mixture soak (or they shake the mixture well, or use a special device called a "Soxhlet extractor" to hasten the process). The fatty part of the mixture will dissolve in the ether. The rest will not. If the ether is then poured off, the fat will be poured off with it. What is left behind is a *fat-free residue*.

Diethyl ether can be easily evaporated because of its low boiling point. A flask of the ether with the fat dissolved in it need merely be placed in a container of hot water. The ether bubbles away[1] and leaves the fat behind. The whole process is called *ether extraction*.

Diethyl ether is a little too inflammable to use in the large quantities that industry would require. Somewhat more complicated ethers called *cellosolves* are used as industrial solvents. They have molecules that contain hydroxyl groups as well as ether combinations.

Tears and Plastics

What if both bonds of the oxygen atom are attached to the same carbon atom? A combination like this is formed: $C=O$. This combination is the *carbonyl group*. Compounds containing it are *carbonyl compounds*.

---

[1] Because ether is so inflammable, it is always evaporated in a special closed area with a fan to suck away the vapors as they are formed. Such a well-ventilated and closed area is called a *hood*. Chemists always use hoods where inflammable or poisonous vapors are being formed during the course of a chemical reaction.

The carbon atom of the carbonyl group has two bonds available for further use. If one of those bonds is attached to a hydrogen atom, the resulting combination is $H — C = O$. Any compound having this combination is an *aldehyde*.

The simplest aldehyde is one in which both spare bonds of the carbonyl group are attached to hydrogen atoms. The resulting molecule looks like this:

Figure 29—Formaldehyde

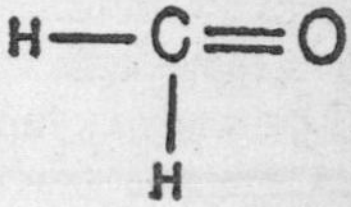

$$H — \underset{\underset{H}{|}}{C} = O$$

It is called *formaldehyde*. If you will compare this molecule with that of methyl alcohol in Chapter 5, you will see that methyl alcohol minus two hydrogen atoms is formaldehyde. Any aldehyde can be produced by taking two hydrogens away from an alcohol (that is, by *dehydrogenating* the alcohol). In fact, that is how the word "aldehyde" arose. It is an abbreviation of "*al*cohol *dehyd*rogenated."

Formaldehyde is a gas with a very strong and irritating odor, which you won't forget once you've smelled it. It irritates the membranes of the eyes, nose, and throat. Get a whiff and your eyes will smart and tear. A substance that will make your eyes tear in this way is known as a *lachrymator* from the Latin word for "tears."

Under the proper conditions, formaldehyde will polymerize into large molecules to form *paraformaldehyde*. This is a solid substance that is easily shipped from place to place and is much more pleasant to handle than the tear-making formaldehyde gas. If paraformaldehyde is heated gently, formaldehyde is formed at once and can then be used.

One of the reasons formaldehyde is so irritating is that it combines easily with proteins, which are the most important compound in all living tissue. By doing so, it hardens tissue and kills it. It also kills any microorganisms that might be present.

Formaldehyde is therefore used to preserve tissues, organs, and even whole organisms. Not only does it prevent decay but it makes the tissue as stiff as a board and easy to handle. Pure formaldehyde is not used, since that is a gas at ordinary temperatures. Instead, a 40 percent solution of formaldehyde in water is used. This solution is called *formalin*. Zoology laboratories in colleges and anatomy laboratories in medical schools always smell of formaldehyde because specimens for dissection are preserved in it. (Formaldehyde is also used in embalming fluids.)

Formaldehyde molecules will combine with phenol molecules under the proper conditions to form a polymer. This polymer, like many organic polymers, has a glassy appearance and is rather brittle. Such polymers are called *resins*.[2] Resins will generally soften on heating. Certain high-boiling substances can be added to the resin to make it soften even more easily. Softened resin can be molded into any desired shape and is then called a plastic. The substance that helps change a resin into a plastic is called a *plasticizer*.

Plastics, after being molded, will become hard upon cooling and will keep their new shape. Some plastics will become soft again when heated and can then be molded into another shape. These are *thermoplastics*. (The prefix "thermo" comes from a Greek word meaning "heat.") Polyethylene, which I mentioned in Chapter 2, is an example of such a plastic.

Other plastics, after being heated and molded, and then cooled, set permanently into shape. If they are heated again, they may char but they will not soften. These are *thermosetting plastics*. The thermosetting plastics are particularly hard and strong, but they tend to be brittle.

Phenol-formaldehyde polymers can be made into thermosetting plastics. The first plastic of this type was developed by the Belgium-born chemist, L. H. Baekeland in 1905. He named the plastic *Bakelite*. Although one of the older plastics,

---

[2] *Natural resins* are the gummy sap of certain trees, usually evergreens. *Rosin* from the sap of the pine tree is the most familiar example. *Myrrh*, which was one of the gifts of the wise men to the Christ-child, is obtained from the sap of certain trees that grow in Arabia and Ethiopia. *Amber* is a hardened resin once formed by an evergreen growing in the Baltic Sea area that is now long extinct. Amber is mined and was much valued in the ancient world as a semi-precious substance. Ornaments are still made of it.

it is also one of the strongest and is still used widely in industry. Plastics in general have grown amazingly in importance. Since the end of World War II, the production of resins and plastics has tripled.

If the two hydrogen atoms of formaldehyde are replaced by two chlorine atoms, the compound that results, *phosgene,* has a much improved odor. In fact, it has a delightful, flowery smell. I smelled a very little bit of it once and I can vouch for that. However, I would much prefer to smell formaldehyde because one good breath of phosgene means death! It causes the lungs to fill with fluid and makes breathing impossible. Phosgene was one of the poison gases used in World War I.

When carbon tetrachloride is used to put out fires, especially fires from electric short-circuits, small quantities of carbon tetrachloride may be changed to phosgene. This is something to be very careful about. Carbon tetrachloride extinguishers should not be used on electrical fires.

Intermediates

In all aldehydes other than formaldehyde, the carbonyl group is attached to only one hydrogen atom. The fourth and last bond of the carbon atom is attached to another carbon atom. As an example, take the two-carbon aldehyde, whose molecule looks like this:

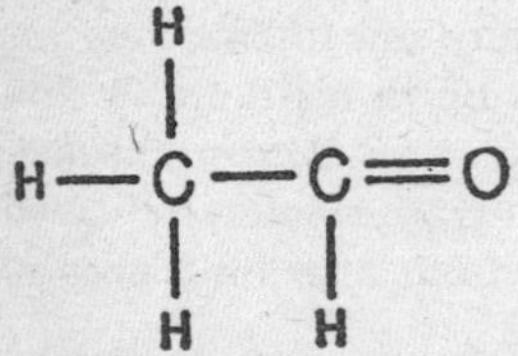

Figure 30—Acetaldehyde

This is *acetaldehyde.* (The official name, using Geneva rules, is *ethanal,* just as formaldehyde should be called *methanal.* The "al" suffix signifies an aldehyde.)

This is a very low-boiling liquid. It boils at 20° C. (68° F.). However, if acetaldehyde is treated with strong acid, the individual molecules hook up in groups of three, forming a ring. This new cyclic compound is *paraldehyde*. In this form, the substance does not boil till a temperature of 122° C. is reached, so that it can be easily shipped from place to place, bottled, and so on. By treating paraldehyde with weak acid, the single acetaldehyde molecules are formed again and are given off as vapor on gentle heating.

Acetaldehyde is an example of a compound that is formed in the human body but is never present except in very small quantities, because as soon as it is formed, it is changed to something else. Compound A is turned to acetaldehyde and then acetaldehyde is turned into compound B. Because acetaldehyde lies in between these two compounds, it is called a *metabolic intermediate*.[3] Although large quantities of it may be formed and then broken down in the body, the amount present at any one time is very small.

One compound that is turned into acetaldehyde by the body is ethyl alcohol. Other simple alcohols are turned into compounds more poisonous than acetaldehyde which is why ethyl alcohol is least harmful. Still acetaldehyde is bad enough. In most people, the acetaldehyde is quickly changed into something else. Some individuals, however, have body chemistries that are a little slow in changing the acetaldehyde once it is formed. In their bodies, acetaldehyde quickly mounts up, and even a small amount of liquor has unpleasant effects.

There are drugs which interfere with the body's handling of acetaldehyde. If these are given to a person who overindulges in alcohol, his next drink will turn out to be a very unpleasant one as the acetaldehyde builds up in his body. A few experiences like that and he may swear off liquor and mean it. Of course, this sort of trick, like any other interference with body chemistry, had better be carried out only on a doctor's advice and under his supervision.

Sleep and Flavor

Paraldehyde is an example of a *sedative*. The word comes from a Latin word meaning "calm" and that is the purpose of

---

[3] The term, *metabolism,* is the name given to all the chemical reactions that take place in living tissue.

a sedative; to relieve nervousness and tension; to make calm. A small quantity of paraldehyde can be given in water and ten or fifteen minutes afterward, the patient is calmed to the point where he has fallen asleep. (A sedative that calms a person to the point of sleep is called a *hypnotic*, from a Greek word, meaning "put to sleep.")

A more effective compound is *chloral* which has a formula like that of acetaldehyde, except that the three hydrogen atoms on the methyl group are replaced by three chlorine atoms. When chloral is dissolved in water, a water molecule adds on to each chloral molecule to form *chloral hydrate*. Chloral hydrate will put a patient to sleep more promptly than paraldehyde will.

These compounds have their disadvantages, however. They have a terrible taste and they irritate the stomach. Furthermore, they can act too quickly and too strongly. Chloral hydrate may be used to prepare what is commonly known as a "knockout drop" or a "Mickey Finn." These days, milder and less harmful sedatives are usually used.

Incidentally, when a sedative such as chloral hydrate is used a number of times, a person may get used to it. He may get to like the calmness and the relief of tension that comes after he has taken it. He may, in fact get to feeling very tense and nervous if he doesn't take a sedative every once in a while. He becomes an "addict."

Addiction to any drug is dangerous and must be avoided. That is one reason why sedatives should not be taken except under a doctor's direction. Another reason is that any sedative, if taken in a carelessly large amount, may make the sleep too deep and turn it into death.

Many aldehydes are quite pleasant one way or another. Some have pleasant odors and are used in perfumes. Others have pleasant tastes and are used in flavors.

Citral, for instance, is a ten-carbon aldehyde, built up of two isoprene units. It has a strong lemon odor and is used in lemon flavorings.

Benzaldehyde is an example of an aromatic aldehyde. That is, its molecule consists of an aldehyde group attached to a benzene ring. Benzaldehyde has a strong almond odor and is used in flavorings and in perfumes.

The most familiar of the aldehydes of this sort also has a benzene ring in its molecule. In addition to an aldehyde group attached to the ring, however, there is also a hydroxyl group and a small ether group. This compound is *vanillin* and it is, of course, the compound that gives vanilla flavoring its pleasant taste. Other aldehydes smell of cinnamon, of lilacs, and so on.

These aldehydes do not dissolve in water but do dissolve in ethyl alcohol. It is for this reason that perfumes and flavoring extracts contain alcohol.

Nobody knows why things smell or taste as they do. It would be nice and simple for the chemist if all aldehydes smelt the same and we could say: "Aha, that is the smell of the aldehyde group." The trouble is they don't all smell the same. They don't even all smell pleasant. Remember formaldehyde.

Diabetes and Perfumes

When the two spare bonds of the carbon atom of a carbonyl group are both attached to other carbon atoms, the resulting compound is a *ketone*. The simplest one is *acetone*, where the two bonds are both attached to methyl groups, thus:

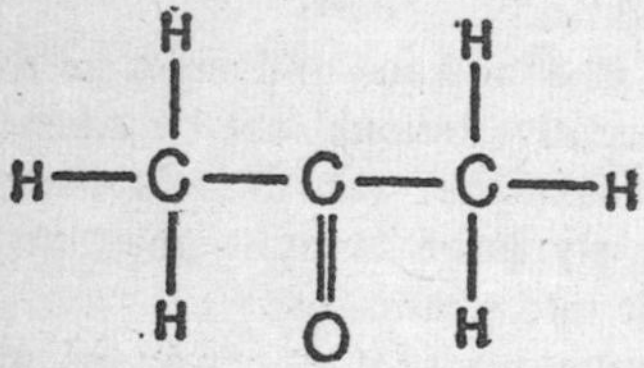

Figure 31—Acetone

The word "ketone" comes from "acetone" and so does the "one" suffix that is the Geneva sign for ketones. The official name for acetone is *propanone*, since it is a three-carbon compound like the hydrocarbon propane.

Acetone will mix with water in all proportions. At the same time, it will dissolve a number of organic compounds that water will not. This makes it very useful as an industrial solvent. Its low boiling point of 56° C. is also helpful.

Acetone, like acetaldehyde, may occur in the body in small quantities. Acetone is not a metabolic intermediate but is formed as the result of a *side reaction*. Compound A, for instance, may usually be converted to Compound B in the body. A very small fraction of it may be, however, converted to Compound C. This minor fraction is the side reaction. Acetone results from such a side reaction.

In the condition known as *diabetes,* there is a shortage in the body of the hormone, insulin. In the absence of insulin, some of the usual chemical changes in the body don't take place properly. It's as though some of the wheels or gears of a machine began to stick. What was previously a side reaction becomes more important as the proper reaction "sticks."

In diabetes, acetone is one of the substances that accumulates in the body because of the improper working of the machinery. It shows up in the urine and, in advanced cases, it leaks into the lungs, and gives the diabetic what is called an "acetone breath." (The odor of acetone is rather pleasant, to be sure, but it is a bad thing to have on your breath if it means advanced diabetes.) [4]

Fortunately, diabetes these days can be treated quite effectively by supplying insulin prepared from the insulin-producing organs of domestic animals. This does not cure the disease but it relieves the symptoms and allows the chemical machinery of the body to continue normally.

Acetone brings to mind another form of unpleasantness. If one of the hydrogen atoms in the acetone molecule is replaced by a bromine atom, the result is *bromacetone*. This is a strong lachrymator, which means, as I said earlier, a tear-producer.

Bromacetone, and other bromine-containing compounds, were used in tear-bombs and tear-shells in World War I. Soldiers with their eyes smarting and blinded with tears are pretty helpless. Even in peacetime such compounds are used

---

[4] Diabetes is an example of a *metabolic disorder.* There are a number of these but diabetes is the most common and therefore the greatest health problem. Diabetes develops during the course of life, sometimes in youth but more often in middle age. Other metabolic disorders are *inborn* or *congenital.* That is, they result from some chemical defect existing in the body from the moment of birth.

by police as *tear gas* to force trapped criminals to surrender and to put down riots without loss of life.

For a noxious gas[5] to be effective, it must be heavier than air. Formaldehyde is noxious enough, for instance, but it is just about as heavy as air. If one army tried to use it against another, the smallest wind would waft it away (perhaps back across the army using it) and break up the gas clouds.

Actually, the most effective noxious gases are not really gases, but liquids. Bromacetone, for instance, boils at 127° C. Such liquids stay put wherever they are scattered by the bomb carrying it. It is the vapors of these liquids that then do the dirty work. The bromacetone vapor is four times as heavy as air so it blows away quite slowly. And as it blows away, more is formed from the liquid.

But enough of that. Some ketones, especially those with rings in their molecules, are much more pleasant to talk about. In *ionone* and *irone* molecules, the carbonyl group is attached to a methyl group on one side and to a more complicated hydrocarbon group, containing a six-carbon ring, on the other. These smell of violets.

A carbonyl group can actually form part of a ring and such a compound is a cyclic ketone. The best-known example is *camphor*, in which the carbonyl group forms part of a six-carbon ring. Camphor is an important plasticizer. It is not uncommon to be able to smell camphor in plastic objects such as combs.

Very unusual cyclic ketones are *muskone* and *civetone*. Muskone occurs in *musk*, which is produced in a small gland near the abdomen of the male musk deer. This creature lives in Central Asia, mostly in the Himalaya region. Apparently the deer uses the musk (which has a powerful scent) to attract the female musk deer, but it also attracts the hunters. Thousands of the deer are killed each year, just for their precious musk. For every 100 deer killed, some 7½ pounds of musk are obtained. This amount of musk contains about an ounce of muskone.

---

[5] The term "noxious" refers to anything that is very unpleasant. It includes poisonous compounds, but also compounds that are blinding, or nauseating, or choking, or sneeze-producing.

The unusual thing about muskone is that the carbonyl group forms part of a ring containing sixteen carbon atoms. When this was discovered, chemists were quite amazed because until then they had been convinced that rings with more than six carbon atoms were quite unstable and not very likely to exist in nature.

Civetone occurs in similar secretions in a gland of the African civet cat. Civetone is like muskone but it goes one better. It is part of a seventeen-carbon ring. Both muskone and civetone (especially the latter) smell rather disgusting when present in quantity. If only a small amount is added to a perfume the effect is pleasant. This is another example of the rule that if a little of a chemical is good, a lot isn't necessarily better.

Actually, perfumery is an art rather than a science. There is no way of predicting odor and perfumes must be blended by trial and error. Even after a blend of compounds has been developed with a most pleasant fragrance, there are problems. The compounds all vaporize easily (or else they would have no odor as a rule). On a warm skin, they will vanish soon, too soon.

Compounds must therefore be added to slow down the vaporization without stopping it. Muskone and civetone do this. They make the perfume clinging and long-lasting, and also strengthen the odor.

Another substance which improves perfume in this way is *ambergris,* a bad-smelling secretion produced by sick whales. Quantities of it are sometimes found in whales or are even cast up on shore. Despite its unappetizing origin and appearance it is immensely valuable because of its use in perfumes.

Perfumes can be diluted in alcohol-water mixtures to form cologne or toilet water. These are cheaper but, of course, don't last as long.

More Vitamins; More Hormones

When two carbonyl groups form part of a six-carbon ring, which also contains two double bonds (so that there are four conjugate double bonds altogether), the result is a *quinone.* The most common quinone is *para-quinone*:

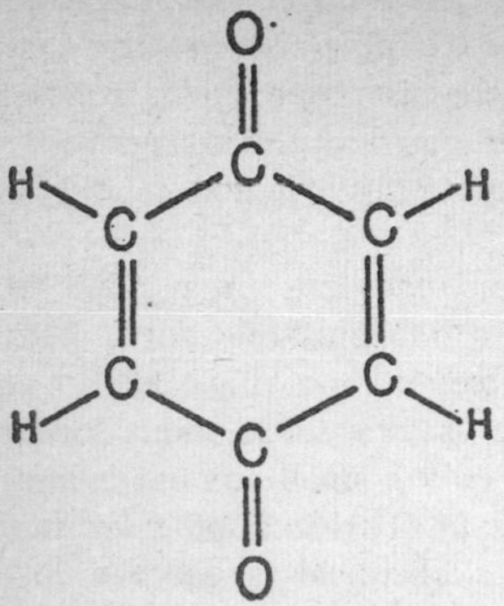

Figure 32—Para-Quinone

The four conjugated bonds give the compound a yellow color. Some of the more complicated quinones are important starting materials for the development of dyes, partly because of their color.

Anthraquinone has a molecule made up of the para-quinone combination shown above with a benzene ring fused on each side of it. If two hydroxyl groups are present on one of the benzene rings of anthraquinone, *alizarin* (also called *Turkey red*) results. This is a red compound one can obtain from the root of a plant known before the days of modern chemistry[6] and it was therefore very valuable. The name, alizarin, comes from an Arabic word meaning simply "the extract," which shows how important the Arabs considered it. They didn't feel it necessary to say which extract—just *the* extract.

To us moderns, however, a far more important quinone is *vitamin K*. Its molecule is built up out of *naphthoquinone*, which is made up of a para-quinone combination with a benzene ring fused on only one side. In vitamin K, the other

[6] Remember that in order to be a good dye, it is not enough that a compound be colored. The compound must also have the ability to combine tightly with the surface of a fabric so that it will not be washed out by water. The color has to be brilliant and not easily faded or changed by the action of air and sun. These are not easy requirements to meet.

side of the naphthoquinone carries a methyl group and a long twenty-carbon chain.

Vitamin K is important to the body because it is used at some point in the clotting of the blood. In the case of accidental bleeding, the blood clots and forms a hard crust at the point of bleeding, thus plugging the leak. If vitamin K is lacking, the machinery of clotting is interfered with, and even a scratch would lead to death by bleeding. (The letter K in the vitamin's name stands for "Koagulation," which is German for "clotting.")

Actually, we don't have to worry about being short of vitamin K. This is one of a number of vitamins which is continually being manufactured by the bacteria that live in our intestines on the food passing by. They make enough for themselves and for us, too. It's a kind of rent they pay for the living quarters and food that we supply.

New-born infants are the only human beings that don't have bacteria swarming in their intestines. Under modern hospital care it takes about three days for the little bugs to establish themselves in the babies. Those three days are a danger period because during that time the infants' bodies do not have the necessary clotting properties, and bleeding could be fatal. For this reason, the mother is usually given vitamin K just before childbirth and enough of it leaks into the baby's bloodstream to protect it. (Of course, for children born outside hospitals under less antiseptic conditions, the danger period of vitamin K deficiency is much shorter.)

Some steroids have carbonyl groups as part of their ring system and are therefore cyclic ketones. A number of the most important hormones are included. Both male and female sex hormones come under this heading. The chief female sex hormone is *estrone*. This consists of a steroid nucleus with one of the carbon atoms in the upper right ring part of a carbonyl group. On the lower left ring is a hydroxyl group.

The chief male sex hormone is *testosterone*. It is formed the opposite way. Its carbonyl group is on the lower left ring and its hydroxyl group is on the upper right.

The adrenal glands (little organs just above each kidney) produce a large number of hormones. All of these have molecules containing the steroid nucleus with one or more carbonyl groups as part of the ring system and one or more hydroxyl groups attached. The most familiar one to the general public is *cortisone*. Its steroid ring system contains three carbonyl groups and two hydroxyl groups.

Cortisone is one of the "wonder drugs" we have heard so much about in recent years. Most of its fame is in connection with its uses in treating some kinds of arthritis. A new adrenal hormone, with very powerful effects on the body, has been discovered recently. It is called *aldosterone* and is unusual because in addition to the carbonyl and hydroxyl groups on the steroid nucleus, it also has an aldehyde side-chain.

Chapter 8

Sweet Substances

A New Kind of Isomerism

THE MOST common carbonyl compounds of all are the sugars. One of the atoms of the carbon chain in a sugar molecule forms part of a carbonyl group. The others all have hydroxyl groups attached. To show what this means I'll write the formulas for two simple sugars (*see Figures 33 and 34*).

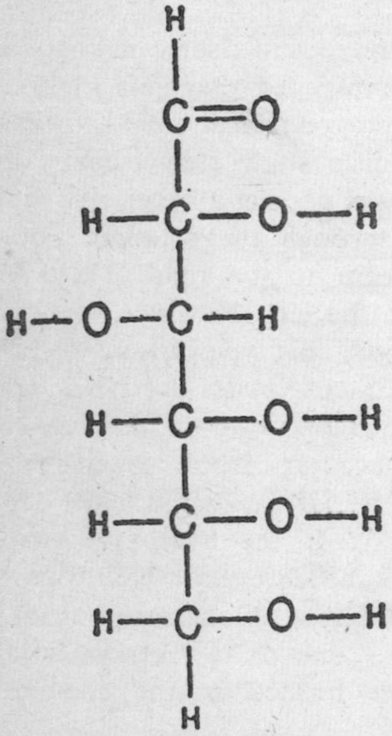

Figure 33—Glucose 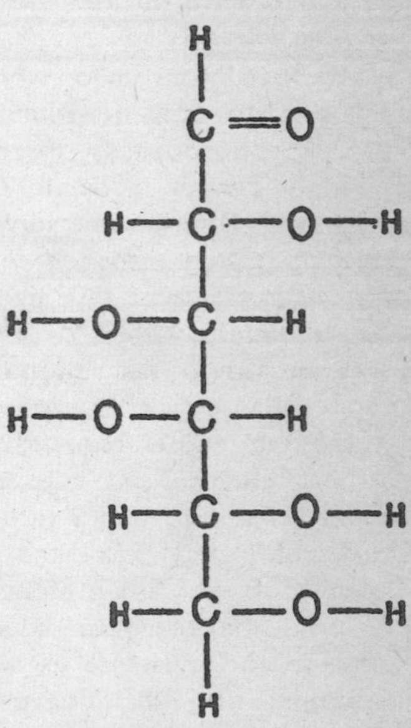   *Figure 34—Galactose*

The molecule on the left is that of *glucose*; the one on the right is that of *galactose*. (The "ose" suffix is generally used for the names of sugars.) If you will look at these two formulas, you will notice that the only difference between them is the direction in which I wrote the hydroxyl group on the fourth carbon from the top.

In most of the formulas that I write in this book, it makes no difference where I put the various atoms as long as I have the bonds arranged correctly. Take the formula for phenol, for instance. There it wouldn't matter whether I attached the hydroxyl group to the top of the ring, or the bottom, or the sides, or whether I pointed it outside the ring or inside the ring.

In other formulas, chemists must be more careful; in the sugars, for instance. Glucose and galactose only differ in the arrangement of the hydroxyl groups but they have different properties because of that. Isomers which differ only in the arrangement of one or more groups in the molecules (without any difference in the nature of the carbon chain) are *stereoisomers.*

The conditions under which stereoisomerism can exist are not easy to explain without complicated diagrams or solid models. Unfortunately, there is no room in the book to deal with the matter in detail. Chemists study stereoisomers by dissolving them in some solvent and passing a beam of a kind of light called *polarized light* through the solution. Some stereoisomers twist this light beam to the right. They are *dextrorotatory.* Others twist it to the left. They are *levorotatory.* Because of this action on light, this type of isomerism is often called *optical isomerism.* Glucose twists polarized light to the right and is frequently called *dextrose,* for that reason.

Both glucose and galactose are six-carbon sugars with aldehyde groups. They are both *aldohexoses* ("aldo" for "aldehyde" and "hex" for "six"). If the hydroxyl groups attached to the carbon atoms are shifted every which way, it turns out that there are sixteen different aldohexoses possible. Glucose and galactose as well as one or two others occur naturally; the others have been formed in the chemical laboratory.

The differences between stereoisomers may seem small, but they are quite important. Most of the compounds in living tissue are of the type that show stereoisomerism and the body can tell one stereoisomer from another very easily. For example, blood contains glucose, but no other hexose.[1] Of all the sixteen aldohexoses, only glucose will do. The average adult has about one-fifth of an ounce of glucose in his blood. This is the energy supply of the human body. The bloodstream carries it to every cell and each cell helps itself to as much glucose as it needs. The cells convert glucose to carbon dioxide and water and make use of the energy that is given off in the process.

You may be wondering how long one-fifth of an ounce can supply the body's needs. The answer is: not long—only about fifteen minutes. Fortunately, though, the body continually makes new glucose and pours it into the bloodstream as the old glucose is used up. The new glucose is, of course, manufactured out of the food we eat.

The blood-sugar level is kept fairly constant. It goes up a bit after we eat, and down a bit if we have been fasting for a while. In fact, it is these small rises and falls that probably result in a feeling of being well-filled or of being hungry.

Insulin, which I've mentioned before, is the hormone that does most to maintain the blood-sugar level. Insulin acts to reduce blood-sugar level. If the blood-sugar level runs high, the insulin production of the body is stepped up. If it runs low, insulin production is held down. (There is another hormone, called *glucagon*, which acts to raise the blood-sugar level. Insulin and glucagon probably work in cooperation.)

Occasionally a particular human being loses the ability to produce all the insulin he needs. He then suffers from the disease, diabetes, which I've also mentioned before. The earliest symptom of that disease which doctors can detect is the fact that a person finds it more and more difficult to keep the blood-sugar down to the proper level.

A doctor tests this by means of a *glucose tolerance test*. The patient is fed a quantity of glucose on an empty stomach. Samples of blood are taken before the feeding and at various times after the feeding. Each time the blood is analyzed for the amount of glucose it contains. In a normal person, the

[1] For this reason, glucose is sometimes called *blood sugar*. It is also called *grape sugar* because it is found in grapes and *corn sugar* because it can be made out of cornstarch.

blood-sugar level goes up after the glucose dose and then down again fairly soon, as the insulin gets to work. In a diabetic, the blood-sugar level goes up higher than in the normal person and comes down much more slowly .

If diabetes continues to get worse, the blood-sugar level may get so high that, in order to remove the sugar, the kidneys pump some of it into the urine. Glucose in the urine is therefore a sure sign of trouble. It can be tested for very simply (and always is when you have a general physical check-up).

Glucose is not the only important sugar in the body. Two others are, in some ways, even more important. These are a pair of *pentoses* (sugars containing five carbons in their molecules). One of these is called *ribose*. Its molecule contains an aldehyde group plus four other carbon atoms each with a hydroxyl group attached. The second pentose is like ribose except that the carbon atom next to its aldehyde group lacks a hydroxyl group. That carbon atom just carries a hydrogen atom where the hydroxyl group ought to be. Since an oxygen atom is missing, it is called *deoxyribose*.

Sugar is Sweet?

So far I have avoided mentioning ordinary sugar, the kind you buy in the stores and put in your coffee or on your cereal. That's because its molecule is a bit more complicated than are those of the sugars I have been talking about.

Two sugar molecules, under the proper conditions, can combine to form a single larger molecule. In doing so, they lose two hydrogen atoms and one oxygen atom, which combine to form a water molecule. What's left of the two sugar molecules combine, forming an ether link. In order to see what I mean, look at the diagram on the following page.

The diagram shows only a piece of each sugar molecule; just one carbon atom of each with its attached groups.

When two molecules combine like this, it is not exactly a polymerization as when isoprene molecules combine to form rubber, though it is sometimes called that. In true polymerization, no atoms are lost during the combination. Here, though, in the sugar combination, atoms are lost.[2] When this happens, the process is known as *condensation*. Organic molecules frequently condense in this way in the body. It is the body's chief way of manufacturing large molecules out of small ones.

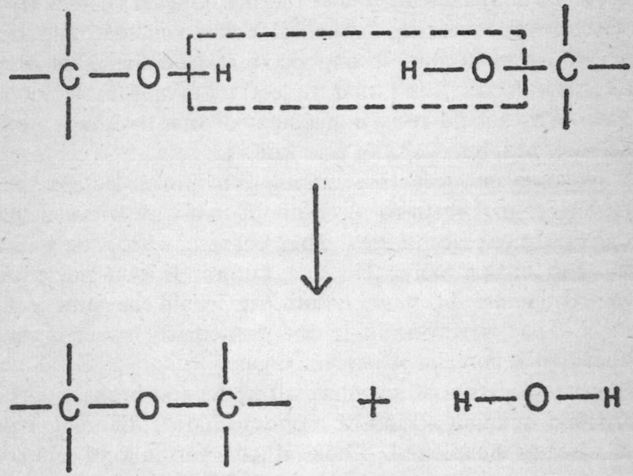

Figure 35—Monosaccharide Condensation

Glucose and galactose are both called *monosaccharides* (from Latin words meaning "one sugar"). When two monosaccharides condense, they form a *disaccharide* ("two sugar"). The particular disaccharide made up of glucose and galactose is called *lactose*. Lactose is the sugar that is found in the milk of all mammals from whales to mice, and it is the only sugar found there. It is commonly called *milk sugar* for that reason. (The name "lactose," in fact, comes from the Latin word for "milk" and "galactose" from the Greek word for "milk.")

[a] In drawing formulas of such reactions, it is customary to put a dotted line around the atom or atom groups that are knocked out of the molecules, as has been done in the formula on this page.

Most kinds of milk, including cow's milk and human milk, contain about 4 percent lactose. A quart of milk, therefore, contains about 1¼ ounces of lactose. Yet with all that sugar, milk is not particularly sweet. It goes to prove how little we understand about sweetness.

Glucose is sweet; not as sweet as ordinary sugar, but still sweet. (You may remember that the prefix "gluc" comes from the Greek word meaning "sweet.") Yet if you rearrange one hydroxyl group in glucose and make it face the other way, you have galactose, and that is less than half as sweet as glucose. Why should the arrangement of one hydroxyl group make such a difference? No one knows.

If glucose and galactose combine to form lactose, you might expect its sweetness to be about half-way between that of the two monosaccharides. That isn't so, either. It is less sweet than either. Why? No one knows. If you put some powdered lactose in your mouth, it would be practically tasteless. That is why milk is not particularly sweet despite the fact that it contains 4 percent sugar.

To get to the kind of sugar we all know and probably love, I must first mention a kind of monosaccharide different from those already mentioned. Look at the formula of glucose again and imagine a similar molecule with the carbonyl group second from the top and the first carbon carrying a hydroxyl group instead. That would be *fructose* or *fruit sugar* (since fructose is found in many fruits and the prefix "fruct" comes from the Latin word for "fruit"). Because fructose twists polarized light to the left it is sometimes called *levulose*.

When glucose and fructose condense, the disaccharide formed is *sucrose*. It is sucrose that is what we all mean when we simply say "sugar."

Sucrose is sweeter than glucose, but fructose is sweeter still. Fructose is the sweetest of the sugars. A teaspoon of fructose in coffee will have as much sweetening effect as 1¾ teaspoons of sucrose, and as much as 2¼ teaspoons of glucose.[3]

---

[3] Of the two sweet compounds I mentioned earlier, glycerol is about as sweet as sucrose and ethylene glycol is actually sweeter. Ethylene glycol is half-way between sucrose and fructose in sweetness.

Breaking Sugar in Two

The juice of all plants contains sucrose. A few plants, such as the sugar cane, sugar beet, and sugar maple contain so much that they are cultivated just for the sugar content. The United States uses up to 100 pounds of sugar each year for every person in the population. About three-fourths of it is *cane sugar* and the rest is mostly *beet sugar*.

Usually, sugar is carefully refined to almost complete purity. Most of the cane sugar we buy is just about 100 percent sucrose. It is pure white and has no taste other than sweetness. *Maple sugar* is purposely not refined all the way. It is a light tan in color and contains small amounts of molecules other than sucrose. It is these impurities that give maple sugar its flavor. Cane sugar need not be refined all the way, either. There are various grades of brown sugar for sale which are often used in cooking because they have flavor in addition to sweetness.

Cane or beet juice from which most of the sugar has been taken out is dark brown in color and is called *molasses*. If sucrose is heated gently, its molecules break up a bit and the color turns brown. This is *caramel*.

Sucrose can be broken down another way, too. Any molecule, in fact, formed by the condensation of two or more simpler molecules, can be broken down without much trouble. This is done by adding water molecules under the right conditions. That exactly reverses the condensation process.

The sucrose molecule, for instance, would add on the two hydrogen atoms and the oxygen atom of water right at the ether combination that hooks the glucose and fructose together. The two halves fall apart. Instead of sucrose, you have a mixture of glucose and fructose molecules. This process of breaking a condensed molecule by the addition of water is called *hydrolysis* (from Greek words meaning "loosen by water"). In the same way, lactose can be hydrolyzed to a mixture of glucose and galactose.

This happens in our intestines, by the way. The sugar in our food is all sucrose except for the sugar in milk and that's lactose. The body can't absorb either of these. However, there are special chemicals in the fluids which are poured into the intestine by certain glands. These chemicals cause the hydrolysis of sucrose and lactose to monosaccharides. The glucose, galactose, and fructose are all absorbed. The galactose and fructose are both changed to glucose by the body and this is one of the ways in which the body's supply of glucose in the blood is kept up.

The process of hydrolyzing large molecules into smaller molecules in our mouth, stomach, and intestines is known as *digestion*.

Chemists can bring about the same type of hydrolysis in the test-tube. For instance, sucrose can be dissolved in water and then made to hydrolyze by adding just a bit of acid. The result is a mixture of glucose and fructose, half-and-half.

The original sucrose twists polarized light to the right. So does glucose, but fructose twists it still more strongly to the left. The final glucose-fructose mixture therefore twists polarized light to the left. While the hydrolysis is proceeding, the direction of twist slowly changes (or "inverts") from right to left. The glucose-fructose mixture is called *invert sugar* for that reason.

Bees prepare invert sugar, by the way. They collect nectar (a fluid in flowers containing small quantities of sucrose). The bees get rid of most of the water and hydrolyze the sucrose to invert sugar which they then store as food. This natural invert sugar is *honey*. Ancient and early medieval Europe did not have sugar, until the Crusaders brought back samples from the Near East. Before that time, the only sweetening agent Europeans had was honey.

Invert sugar is sweeter than sucrose because of its fructose content, so it is frequently used in candies, making them less expensive. A given amount of sucrose can be spread over more candies if it is hydrolyzed to invert sugar first. In fact, you may wonder why we bother with sucrose? Why don't we all use invert sugar instead, or even just fructose? Then we could use less of it in desserts. The desserts would be just as sweet, and considerably less fattening.[4]

---

[4] Fructose would be especially useful to people with diabetes. Such people must ration their sugar with the greatest care because they can't handle the glucose it contains without insulin. Fructose, however, can be handled by the body even without insulin.

Unfortunately, there are two catches. Pure fructose is expensive; it costs nearly four dollars a pound. Secondly, fructose absorbs moisture from the air. Sucrose does not. If the sucrose in your sugar bowl is in the form of fine crystals, it stays that way and always pours easily. If it were fructose instead, or even invert sugar, it might begin as fine crystals but it would quickly absorb water and set into a hard lump that couldn't be used.

Giant Molecules

There is no reason why condensation of monosaccharides should stop at the disaccharide stage. Living organisms can take glucose molecules and condense them in large numbers to form a giant molecule. Such a molecule may be made up of thousands of glucose residues strung end to end. These residues may be all in a straight line, or they may be arranged in branches of different lengths and complications. Such molecules do not contain entire glucose units since water has been split out at each point of union between glucose molecules. What is left over is a glucose *residue*. The same term is used for other types of molecules which are condensed to form giant molecules (sometimes called *macromolecules*).

One group of such molecules is lumped under the name of *starch*. It is an example of a *polysaccharide* ("many sugar"). As the glucose molecules are condensed to form starch, the sugary characteristics are lost. Starch does not dissolve in water as the sugars do. Nor is starch sweet; it is completely tasteless.

Plants store their food supply in the form of starch, particularly for the use of the next generation. Seeds such as kernels of corn and ears of various grains are starchy. So are special roots like those of potatoes, yams, and carrots, out of which new plants will grow. Starch is a compact storage molecule, holding glucose residues in a form that will not dissolve in the cell fluids. The plant has methods for breaking up the starch molecule (that is, hydrolyzing it) back into glucose when needed.

The starch is broken down in stages. In sprouting grain, called *malt*, the giant molecules of starch are hydrolyzed to smaller pieçes called *dextrins*. Eventually, the molecules are broken down to the disaccharide stage, containing only two glucose residues apiece. This disaccharide is called *maltose*. Finally, maltose is broken down to glucose.

Dextrins and maltose are used in babies' formulas. Infants cannot drink cow's milk just as it comes from the cow. Cow's milk is for calves, not for babies. It has too much of certain tissue-building substances for the baby to handle. For that reason, cow's milk is mixed with a certain amount of boiled water to dilute it properly. In doing so, the lactose content is also diluted and becomes too little for the baby's needs. Sugar in one form or another must be added. Most frequently, a mixture of dextrins and maltose[5] is used. It is soluble and only very slightly sweet so that the taste of the milk is not altered.

The animal body also stores its glucose whenever it has more than it needs at the moment. The starch in the food you eat is hydrolyzed to glucose in your intestines and that is absorbed. After an average meal, the body absorbs far more glucose than is required for the immediate use of the body. It takes the excess and condenses it into a special kind of starch called *glycogen* or *animal starch*. This is stored in the muscles and skin, but mainly in the liver. A well-nourished adult may have as much as twelve ounces of glycogen stored here and there in his body.

In between meals, glycogen is broken down to glucose and dribbled into the bloodstream at just the right rate to keep the blood-sugar level steady.[6] (The word "glycogen" comes from Greek words meaning "gives rise to sweetness," that is, to sugar.)

There is enough glycogen in a well-nourished body to keep it going for as long as eighteen hours. Of course, people can

[5] The mixture is usually prepared from cornstarch and is marketed either as a powder or as a syrup.

[6] It is one of the jobs of insulin to see that this rate is indeed "just the right rate." The hormone adrenalin, on the other hand, speeds up the breakdown of glycogen so that there is an extra supply of glucose in the blood for quick emergency energy. That is why the adrenalin supply in the body goes up in moments of anger, fear, or passion.

go without eating for much longer than that, because energy is also stored as fat.

Our Debt to Bacteria and Herbs

All the monosaccharides, disaccharides, and polysaccharides that I have mentioned are lumped together under the name of *carbohydrates*.[7] All the carbohydrates I have described so far are nutritious. Some, however, are not.

Glucose molecules, for instance, can be condensed in a slightly different manner than that which produces starch. The giant molecule produced by this different way of linking glucose together is called *cellulose*.

Cellulose is tough and stringy and will form thread-like *fibers*. Cellulose is the stiffening agent in *wood*.[8] Plants form layers of cellulose between their cells; hence the name "cellulose." Cellulose in plants helps to make the plant structure rigid just as bones and shells do in animals.

Sometimes plants produce cellulose in a purer state than that in which it is found in wood. They produce it in fibrous form to protect seeds, for instance. The best known example is *cotton*, which is about 90 percent cellulose. Other vegetable fibers—*linen, hemp*, and so on—are also cellulose.

Once cellulose is separated out of wood in the form of wood pulp, it can be formed into thin, flexible sheets called *paper*. Cellulose can also be combined with certain chemicals

[7] Here is one place where it is wiser not to explain where a name comes from. The name was coined at a time when chemists had the wrong notion of the structure of carbohydrate molecules. It does sometimes happen, you see, that chemists may name a substance and then find out later that their reasons for choosing such a name were wrong. By then, it is usually too late to do anything about it. Common names like "oxygen" and "vitamin" were mistakes.

[8] Wood is about half cellulose. The rest consists of molecules made up of chains of sugars other than glucose. These molecules are called *hemicelluloses*. There are also giant molecules made up of chains of a fairly complicated alcohol, and these, which are not carbohydrates at all, are called *lignin*. When wood is treated so that the hemocelluloses and lignin are removed, and only the cellulose remains, the result is *wood pulp*.

to form a thick liquid called *viscose*. This can be squeezed through thin slots or through tiny holes and then converted back to cellulose. The new cellulose has molecules only about one-eighth the size of the original and is called *regenerated cellulose*. If the viscose was squeezed through a slot, the regenerated cellulose forms a flexible transparent sheet called *cellophane*. If it was squeezed through holes, it forms a synthetic cellulose fiber called *viscose rayon*, which is glossier than natural cellulose fibers. Ordinary cotton can be given a silky appearance by treatment with a strong chemical called sodium hydroxide. This is called *mercerized cotton*, so named for John Mercer who first discovered the process in 1844.

In one way, cellulose fails us. We cannot be nourished by it. We eat it, to be sure, since most plant foods have a certain amount of cellulose. Some, such as the leafy vegetables, consist of almost nothing but cellulose, hemicellulose, and water. Unfortunately, our bodies have no chemical machinery for hydrolyzing cellulose to glucose. Cellulose in our diet just acts as bulk or roughage, and supplies no nourishment.

No animal visible to the naked eye—not even termites—can digest cellulose. Certain microscopic one-celled animals, called protozoa, can, however. This explains how termites can live on a diet of wood. Protozoa living in termite intestines can hydrolyze the cellulose. The protozoa use some of the glucose they produce and the termite uses the rest. Without the protozoa, the termites would die.[9]

Grazing animals usually have very long intestines or special places (such as extra stomachs) where food can be stored for quite a while. This gives bacteria in the intestines of cattle, for instance, a chance to hydrolyze the cellulose of grass to glucose. In this way, cattle can live on grass. After that, of course, human beings can live on cattle, so we owe a

[9] When two organisms live together and help each other, the process is known as *symbiosis,* from Greek words meaning "life together." Our own intestinal bacteria produce vitamins and so are a bit symbiotic. When one form of life takes from another form and gives nothing in exchange except, often, a lot of trouble, that's *parasitism.* Disease bacteria are examples of parasites.

debt to the bacteria, too. Beefsteak is only one step removed from grass.

Sugars need not condense only with other molecules like themselves. A glucose molecule, for instance, can condense with any molecule possessing a hydroxyl group. It can condense with alcohols, phenols, sterols and so on. Such a condensation between a sugar and a non-sugar gives a compound called a *glycoside*.

Many glycosides occur naturally in various plants. A number of these have strong effects of one sort or another on the body. For that reason, they are sometimes used in medicine.

The most familiar of these are the *cardiac glycosides*. They are called that because they affect the action of the heart and "cardiac" comes from a Greek word meaning "heart."

The cardiac glycosides are derived from a plant called the foxglove. The leaves of the foxglove, from which the compounds are derived, are thin and joined together at the stems, something like fingers. The mixture of glycosides obtained from them are therefore called *digitalis*, from the Latin word for "finger."

Digitalis is made up of glycosides containing rather odd sugars. Some of them are missing one or two hydroxyl groups and several don't occur in any other type of compound. These sugars are condensed with certain sterols.

Digitalis is an example (and not the only one) of an "old wives' remedy" that became respectable. Throughout history people (usually old women with many years of practical experience) have been gathering "herbs" which they then used to prepare medicines for treating various ailments. As the science of medicine grew, these herb-remedies were rather sneered at.

In 1785, however, when Dr. William Withering (a British physician) introduced the use of digitalis into modern medicine, he admitted that he got his information originally from one of these old women who used foxglove extracts as a secret remedy.

Of course, cardiac glycosides can help people with heart trouble only when carefully prescribed in small quantities by a doctor. In larger quantities, the drug can kill. The glycosides are sometimes used as rat poisons for that reason and in earlier times they were used on arrows to make the arrow-wound deadly.

Chapter 9

Sour Substances

Acids and Ants

A CARBON can be part of a carbonyl group and, at the same time, be attached to a hydroxyl group. The result would be this:

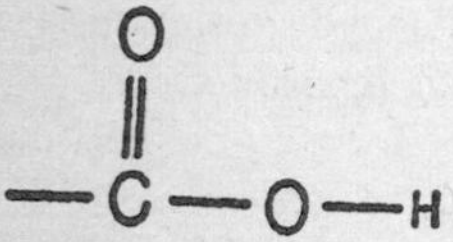

Figure 36—The Carboxyl Group

Such a combination of atoms is called a *carboxyl group*.

Perhaps you may remember that in Chapter 6, I said that a hydrogen atom attached to an oygen atom had a certain tendency to come off as a hydrogen ion. I also said that a compound in which the hydrogen atom could do this was an acid and that the easier it was for hydrogen ions to fall off, the stronger the acid. Phenols, for instance, are stronger acids than ordinary alcohols are.

It turns out that a hydrogen ion can escape from a carboxyl group a million times more easily than from the hydroxyl group of a phenol. Any organic compound that contains a carboxyl group is therefore distinctly acid in its properties. For this reason, such compounds are called *carboxylic acids*.

Don't be fooled, though! The carboxylic acids may be a million times stronger than phenols, but they are millions and millions of times weaker than certain very strong inorganic acids. On the whole, therefore, the carboxylic acids, as a group, are still considered "weak acids."

Look at the formula for the carboxyl group and you will see that the carbon atom still has one bond left to use in hooking on another atom. This additional atom could be hydrogen, in which case *formic acid*[1] results.

Formic acid is one of the strongest of the carboxylic acids. It is ten times as strong as almost any of the others. It is that much more irritating to living tissues as a result. The red ant injects a small quantity of formic acid into the body when it bites, which is quite bothersome. (The word "formic" comes from the Latin word for "ant.") It is also found in nettles and is the reason why it is better not to touch nettles.

Look at the formula of the carboxyl group again. If you remove the hydroxyl group and replace it with a hydrogen atom, an aldehyde group results. Aldehydes which are related to a carboxylic acid in this way are usually named after the acid. For instance, if the hydroxyl group in formic acid is replaced by a hydrogen atom, formaldehyde results and that, in fact, is why the compound is called formaldehyde.

Furthermore, if the carbon atom of formic acid is attached to three chlorine atoms instead of to an oxygen and a hydroxyl group, the result is "chloroform." This is an example of how names spread from one compound to another so that the original meaning of the name is lost. After all, what does chloroform (or iodoform) have to do with ants?

Vinegar

The carboxyl group can be attached to a carbon atom. If that carbon atom is part of a methyl group, the result is:

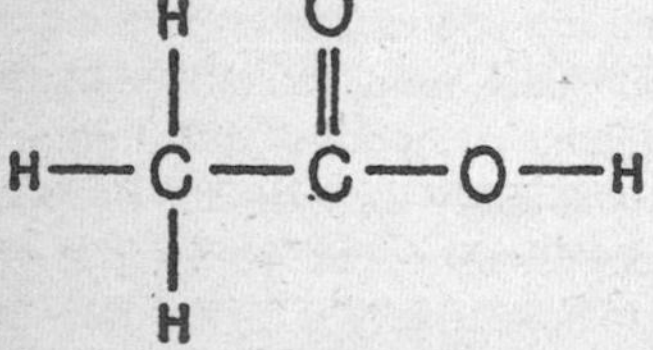

Figure 37—Acetic Acid

This is *acetic acid*.

Like ethyl alcohol, acetic acid has been known since pre-

---

[1] The Geneva nomenclature for carboxylic acids uses the suffix "-oic acid." Formic acid would be called *methanoic acid*.

historic times. The pure substance itself wasn't prepared until 1700, but before that it was known as a solution in water. This is due, once again, to the action of micro-organisms.

Certain such microscopic creatures, called yeasts, are responsible for the conversion of sugar or starch into alcohol. If apple juice is exposed to these little creatures, a kind of apple wine, called *cider*, is formed. The ethyl alcohol content of cider can be as high as 15 percent. If cider is now exposed to a special type of bacterium, the ethyl alcohol is changed to acetic acid.

Compare the formula of ethyl alcohol in Chapter 5 with that of acetic acid. Both as you see, are two-carbon compounds. In both, the right-hand carbon atom has a hydroxyl group attached. To change ethyl alcohol to acetic acid, it is only necessary to remove two hydrogen atoms and replace them with an oxygen atom. The chemical machinery in living tissue can do this sort of thing quite easily. Most organisms (including ourselves) change acetic acid into other things. The value of the particular bacterium used in treating cider is that it allows the acetic acid to accumulate without changing it further.

In other words, cider (and other wines, too), on being allowed to stand, becomes sour because an acid is formed. In ancient and medieval times when wine-making wasn't scientifically controlled, cheap wine was almost always sour. "Sour wine" in Old French is "vin egre," and from that comes our term *vinegar*. The vinegar we buy in stores contains about 3 to 6 percent acetic acid. It is the acetic acid that gives vinegar its odor and its sour taste.

The word "acid" comes from a Latin word meaning "sour," while the word "acetic" comes from the Latin word for "vinegar" which is itself probably derived from the word for "sour." The meaning of "acetic acid" is thus "sour sour." This isn't bad considering that acetic acid was probably the first acid known to man and sourness is the most noticeable thing about acids.

The prefix "acet" is also given to the names of other two-carbon compounds which have a chemical relationship to acetic acid. Examples are acetaldehyde and acetylene.

If some of the hydrogen atoms of the methyl group of

acetic acid are replaced by halogen atoms, the strength of the acid is increased. If all the hydrogen atoms are replaced by chlorine atoms, the resulting compound, *trichloracetic acid*, is some five thousand times as strong an acid as acetic acid itself. In fact, it is just about the strongest organic acid in common use by chemists.

If one of the hydrogen atoms of the methyl group of acetic acid is replaced by fluorine, the result is *fluoroacetic acid*. In combination with a sodium ion, it forms an excellent rat-killer. Unfortunately, it is also an excellent anything-else-killer even in small quantities so it must be used very cautiously.

Two at a Time

The carboxyl group can be attached to a hydrocarbon chain of any length. As far as the naturally occurring carboxylic compounds are concerned, however, the total number of carbon atoms present is almost always even. Acetic acid has two carbon atoms, for instance. Other naturally occurring carboxylic compounds contain four carbon atoms, six, eight, and so on, up to more than twenty. Similar compounds with odd numbers of carbon atoms are hardly ever found.

The reason for this is that living organisms manufacture the carboxylic acids they need by beginning with acetic acid[2] (which they can make out of sugar or starch). To the acetic acid, they add other molecules of acetic acid. Since a two-carbon compound is begun with and other two-carbon combinations are added, the compounds that result must have even numbers of carbon atoms.

The naturally occurring carboxylic acids form a part of the molecules of the fatty and oily substances found in plants and animals. For this reason, they are often called *fatty acids*.[3]

[2] Once acetic acid is formed from carbohydrate in the body, it can be broken down all the way to carbon dioxide and water. It can also be used as a building block to form not only larger carboxylic acids but also steroids or, for that matter, carbohydrate once again. Acetic acid, in a way, may be considered the chief chemical crossroad in the body machinery.

[3] The smallest carboxylic acid having "fatty acid" properties may be considered to be the three-carbon acid which is called *propionic*

The fatty acids are among the earliest organic compounds known to chemists and most of the naturally occurring ones were named before any idea of proper nomenclature was established. Instead of being named in such a way as to give a clue to their molecular structure, they were usually named after the particular fat from which they were first obtained or for some other non-structural reason.

For instance, the four-carbon fatty acid (remember that one of the carbon atoms is always part of a carboxyl group) is called *butyric acid*, because it can be obtained from butter. (The "but" prefix was then given to other four-carbon compounds also, as, for instance, to butane.)

The most noticeable thing about butyric acid is its odor, which is very unpleasant. Sometimes, when butter is allowed to stand too long, some of its molecules hydrolyze and break up. A small quantity of butyric acid is released and the butter is then said to have become rancid. If you have ever smelled rancid butter, you need no further details.

The smell is also prominent in the next more complicated fatty acids, the ones with six, eight, and ten carbon atoms. These are called *caproic acid, caprylic acid,* and *capric acid.* Each one gets its name from the Latin word for "goat." Those of you who have ever smelled a billy goat need no further description there, either. If you haven't got a goat handy, try Limburger cheese. That has capric acid in it.

These acids are found only to a small extent as part of fat molecules. Fat molecules, when hydrolyzed, usually give rise to fatty acids with considerably longer chains. The most common ones, for instance, are fatty acids with chains made up of sixteen or eighteen carbon atoms. The sixteen-carbon acid is *palmitic acid,* which was first obtained from the oil of the palm tree. The one with eighteen carbon atoms is *stearic acid,* the name coming from the Grek word for solid, because it was obtained from solid fats.

The smaller fatty acids are liquid at room temperature. Caprylic acid, for instance, melts at 16° C. (59° F.). When

---

acid from the Greek words meaning "first fat." That is why the three-carbon hydrocarbon is called "propane," using the "prop" prefix.

the number of carbon atoms is ten or more, however, the fatty acid is solid. Stearic acid doesn't melt until it reaches 69° C. (158° F.).

The melting point doesn't depend only on the length of the carbon chain, however. Stearic acid, as I've said, has a molecule containing a chain of eighteen carbon atoms. Only single bonds are involved. Stearic acid is a saturated fatty acid. Unsaturated fatty acids also exist. In fact, the most common fatty acid of all is *oleic acid*. It also has a molecule with eighteen carbon atoms, but right in the middle of that chain is one double bond. That one double bond makes a lot of difference. While stearic acid melts at 69° C. and is solid at room temperature, oleic acid melts at 13° C. (55° F.) and is a liquid on any mild day.

Linoleic acid and *linolenic acid* are more extreme cases. Both have molecules with eighteen carbon atoms, but linoleic acid has two double bonds and linolenic acid has three double bonds. Both melt at temperatures below zero Centigrade. *Arachidonic acid* has twenty carbon atoms and four double bonds, and is also low-melting.

The human body can build its own saturated fatty acids easily. (That's the reason starchy foods are so fattening. The body breaks down the starch to acetic acid and then works that up again to fatty acids which are incorporated into fat molecules.) The body can also put one double bond into the fatty acid chain and make its own oleic acid. However, the body seems unable to put more than one double bond into the molecule.

This means the body can't form its own linoleic acid, linolenic acid, or arachidonic acid. It is the arachidonic acid that we particularly need (no one knows why, I must add), but if we get linoleic acid or linolenic acid to start with, we can go the rest of the way. At least one of these extra-unsaturated fatty acids must be present in the diet as part of the fat molecules. In their absence, children sometimes develop skin disorders. (Before they knew what caused this, chemists talked of a "Vitamin F" but that name has now been abandoned.)

Because these particular fatty acids are needed in the diet for good health, they are sometimes called the *essential fatty acids.* Just remember, though, that the word "essential" means "essential in the diet."

An example of a carboxylic acid that is definitely not a fatty acid is *benzoic acid.* Its molecules consist of a carboxyl group attached to a benzene ring. It was first isolated from gum benzoin[4] back in 1608 and that is how it got its name. The "benz" prefix stuck to other similar compounds, including benzene itself. In small quantities, *sodium benzoate,* which is benzoic acid that has been treated with sodium hydroxide, is used as a food preservative.

Soda Water and Spinach

The spare bond of the carboxyl group may be attached to a hydroxyl group, thus:

Figure 38—Carbonic Acid

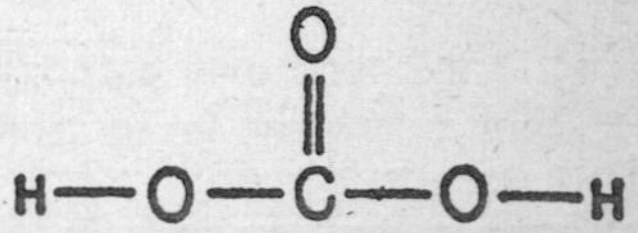

This compound is *carbonic acid.*

Carbonic acid is quite unstable. It can't exist pure. (If you tried to make it pure, its molecules would break apart into the simpler molecules of water and carbon dioxide.) It can exist in solution, that is, mixed with water, but even then most of the molecules break down.

Soda water is water with carbon dioxide dissolved in it. The carbon dioxide (which is a gas) is dissolved under pressure so that more of it will mix with the water. When the pressure is relieved by uncapping the bottle, the extra carbon dioxide bubbles out. It is the small quantity of carbonic acid formed by the combination of a little of the carbon dioxide with water that gives the soda water its pleasant tart taste.

The molecule of carbonic acid can lose both hydrogens. If one hydrogen ion is removed, what is left is the *bicarbonate ion.* The second hydrogen is about a thousand times as

---

[4] This is the sap of a tree in Southeast Asia and Indonesia. The word "benzoin" may be a corruption of "Benjamin."

difficult to remove as the first. When that goes also then what is left is the *carbonate ion*. In the human bloodstream and in the tissues themselves, carbonic acid, bicarbonate ion, and dissolved carbon dioxide are all present, but not carbonate ion.

Bicarbonate ion and carbonate ion often link up with the ions of certain metals. The compounds that result, although they contain carbon, have many similarities to inorganic compounds. For instance, *calcium*[5] *carbonate* is a mineral commonly called *limestone*. It also occurs in the rather beautiful form of *marble*. Living creatures can manufacture calcium carbonate. It forms the skeleton of small animals called the corals[6] as well as the shells of clams, oysters, snails and birds' eggs.

Sodium carbonate is found in many kitchens under its common name, *washing soda*. *Sodium bicarbonate* is even more likely to be found there. It is commonly called *baking soda*.

The spare bond of a carboxyl group may also be attached to a second carboxyl group, thus:

Figure 39—Oxalic acid

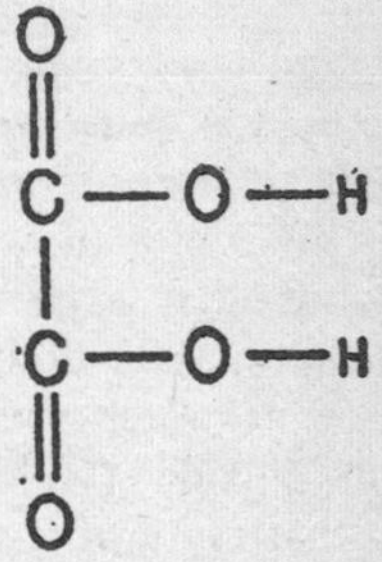

This is *oxalic acid* (a name derived from the Latin name for the wood sorrel, a plant in which it occurs).

[5] Calcium is a light, silvery metal which is very active, but not quite as active as sodium and potassium. The calcium atom loses two electrons to become calcium ion. In the human body, calcium ion occurs in bones and teeth.

[6] Some people think the limestone deposits in the earth are the packed skeletons of billions upon billions of such animals. Such skeletons certainly form the coral reefs of the South Pacific.

Oxalic acid can lose first one hydrogen ion, then another, just as carbonic acid can. When both hydrogen ions are gone, what is left is *oxalate ion*. This can combine with calcium ion to form *calcium oxalate*.

Calcium oxalate is very insoluble and that makes it useful to chemists at times. Chemists are sometimes interested in knowing how much calcium ion is present in some substance. They dissolve the substance in water. (If necessary, they first treat the substance in such a way as to make it soluble.) Once it is in solution, they add a quantity of some compound which contains oxalate ion as part of its molecule. The oxalate ion promptly combines with all (or just about all) of the calcium ion present. The calcium oxalate, being insoluble, *precipitates*; that is, it comes out of solution as a fine white powder and settles to the bottom of the container. The chemist can separate out this powder and weigh it very accurately. From its weight, he can tell how much calcium ion was present in a sample of the original mixture. This is an example of *chemical analysis*.

Sometimes calcium oxalate forms under less useful circumstances. The body forms oxalate ion in small quantities as part of the regular working of its chemistry. Some oxalate ion appears in the urine as a consequence.[7] There is always considerable calcium ion finding its way into the urine also. Therefore calcium oxalate forms. Ordinarily, the small crystals

---

[7] One of the ways the body has of getting rid of unwanted or harmful substances is through the urine. Blood passing through the kidneys is continually being filtered. A quantity of water plus dissolved material enters the kidney tubules (microscopic tubes) from the blood. Material needed by the body, such as glucose, is reabsorbed back into the bloodstream as the solution works its way down the tubule. As much water as possible is also reabsorbed so that not too much is wasted. Just enough water is left in the kidney to keep the waste material well dissolved plus an extra amount if the body has been well supplied with liquids in the previous hours. There are at least tiny quantities of a great many chemicals in the urine. Most of these are waste products but not all are. Some are useful materials which have "spilled over." (The body's method of reclaiming useful products in the tubules is rarely perfect.) By studying the urine it is sometimes possible to learn about the disorders of a person's chemical machinery. I've already mentioned diabetes as one example of this.

of calcium oxalate are kept from joining one another some-how. (Chemists are not sure just exactly how.) In a few people, however, something goes wrong and the crystals jam together to form a small hard "stone." These can block the tubes leading from the kidney. Such *kidney stones*[8] can be extremely painful and sometimes surgery is necessary to remove them.

Some foods—spinach and rhubarb, for instance—contain quantities of oxalic acid or oxalate ion. In fact, rhubarb leaves contain so much oxalate as to be poisonous. (The stalks are all right, though.) The spinach, of course, is sup-posed to be "good for you." But the presence of oxalic acid in spinach makes it less good than most people think it is. Oxalic acid ties up calcium that could otherwise be used to build bones. Some of the iron which spinach contains is also tied up with oxalic acid and can't be used by the body.

A more complicated compound with two carboxyl groups is *adipic acid*. It has four carbons between the two groups and it is used in the preparation of Nylon.

More Isomerism

Two simple dicarboxylic compounds (that is, compounds like oxalic acid which contain two carboxyl groups in the molecule) are *succinic acid* and *fumaric acid*. Both are impor-tant intermediates in the body. The molecule of succinic acid contains four carbon atoms, the two end ones both being parts of carboxyl groups. Fumaric acid has a similar molecule except that there is a double bond in the middle of the chain.

Fumaric acid gives me a chance to explain about still another form of isomerism, which occurs sometimes (but not always) when a double bond exists in the molecule. A mole-cule like that of fumaric acid can be written in two ways. The formula in Figure 40 is that of fumaric acid. The one in Figure 41 represents a different compound with different

---

[8] Calcium oxalate stones are not the only type of kidney stones or even the most dangerous type. Calcium phosphate stones are perhaps more dangerous but these are not made up of organic compounds so I won't talk about them in this book.

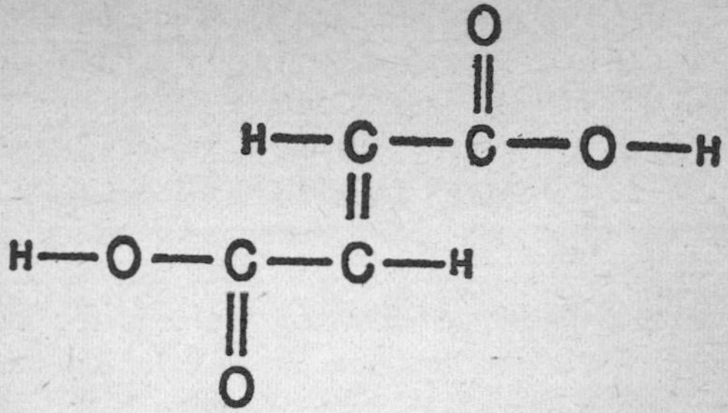

Figure 40—
Fumaric Acid

$$H-C-C-O-H$$
$$\text{(with } =O \text{ on the right carbon)}$$
$$H-O-C-C-H$$

properties. It is called *maleic acid*. The only difference between them is the direction in which the carboxyl groups point with respect to each other. In fumaric acid, the carboxyl groups are on opposite sides of the double bond, across from

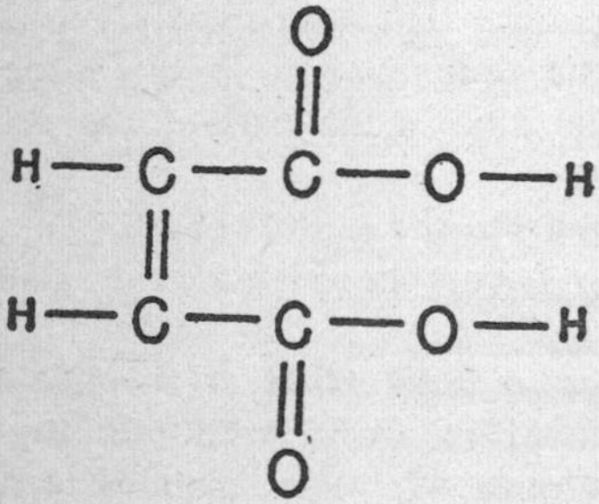

Figure 41—Maleic Acid

one another. It is a *trans* isomer ("trans" being Latin for "across"). In maleic acid, the carboxyl groups are on the same side of the double bond. It is a *cis* isomer ("cis" being Latin for "on this side").

This sort of thing is called *cis-trans isomerism*.[9] It is very important to the body in connection with compounds like vitamin A and steroids which have double bonds. A *cis* isomer of a compound may have a potent effect on the body whereas the *trans* isomer may have little or no effect—or vice versa.

[9] *Cis-trans* isomers do not necessarily affect polarized light, so they are not optical isomers, as glucose and galactose are.

Chapter 10

Fruit, Muscle and Soap

The Pleasant Acids

A FOOD which is sour or tart is sure to contain som
carboxylic acid. Fruits are good examples.

Malic acid is found in unripe pears, apples, and oth
fruits. The amount of acid grows less and the sugar conte
increases as a fruit ripens. This is why ripe fruits taste s
much better than unripe fruits. This is also useful to th
plant itself. It is only after the fruit is ripe, and the seeds
contains are thoroughly mature, that animals will eat it. A
the fruit is eaten (or some time afterward) the seeds a
scattered and spread about. That is the part of the proce
that is useful to the plant.

The word "malic" comes from the Latin word for "apple
and the "mal" prefix also occurs in related acids such s
maleic acid.

The molecule of malic acid is like that of succinic aci
being made up of a four-carbon chain with the two e
carbons part of carboxyl groups. However, malic acid has
hydroxyl group attached to one of the middle carbon atom
It is thus an example of a *hydroxy-acid*. Like succinic aci
malic acid is an important intermediate in the body.

A similar compound, *tartaric acid,* is found in grape
Its molecule is also like that of succinic acid and malic aci
but it has two hydroxyl groups, one attached to each of th
middle carbon atoms. Tartaric acid has a pleasant functio
in the kitchen. In order to make bread and pastry light, fluff
and nice to eat, the dough must be puffed up with some so
of gas and filled with millions of small bubbles. (Look at
piece of bread or cake and see for yourself.)

The oldest way of doing this was to make use of a sma
quantity of yeast. Yeast, as I said earlier in the book, is
microscopic plant that can convert some of the starch «

flour to ethyl alcohol. In doing this, it also produces the gas, carbon dioxide. If the yeast is allowed to remain in the dough for a while and is kept warm, a bit of ethyl alcohol and carbon dioxide are produced and trapped throughout the dough. If the dough is then warmed a little more and finally baked, it "rises." The heat causes the carbon dioxide to expand and the ethyl alcohol to turn into a vapor which also expands. The dough gets all bubbly and foamy and stays that way.

Carbon dioxide obtained in any other way will serve as well. A housewife can make her own carbon dioxide, for instance, by using *baking powder*.

Baking powder contains two important ingredients: bicarbonate ion (in the form of sodium bicarbonate) and a weak acid such as tartaric acid. You may remember that bicarbonate ion is carbonic acid with a hydrogen ion removed. Well, the effect of tartaric acid (or of other such weak acids) is to put the hydrogen ion back onto the bicarbonate ion and form carbonic acid once more. This only happens if the baking powder is mixed with the batter being prepared for baking. The baking powder dissolves in the water content of the batter and it is then that the carbonic acid is formed.

If the batter is heated, the carbonic acid molecules rapidly break up to carbon dioxide and water. The expanding carbon dioxide gas then forms the necessary bubbles in the pastry. Self-rising flours have the baking powder already mixed in with the rest of the ingredients.

The most common organic acid found in fruits is *citric acid*. The connection of the name with citrus fruits is obvious and that's where it was first found. It is present in many other fruits, too, however. The molecule of citric acid contains a hydroxyl group and no less than three carboxyl groups so it is an example of a *tricarboxylic acid*.

Citric acid is another one of the important intermediates in the human body. In fact, the most important set of energy-producing reactions in the body is called the *tricarboxylic acid cycle,* because citric acid is involved.[1] Sometimes it is actually called the *citric acid cycle*.

[1] Involved in the tricarboxylic acid cycle are some of the compounds I mentioned previously: succinic acid, malic acid, and

Sour Milk and Tired Muscles

Milk, even pasteurized milk, always contains a number of microorganisms. If allowed to stand at room temperature, these germs will multiply. Some of them get the energy to do so by breaking the lactose molecule, which, remember, is the particular sugar found in milk, into four parts. The broken bits are *lactic acid*. Lactic acid is a hydroxy-acid with a molecule that looks like this (*see Figure 42*):

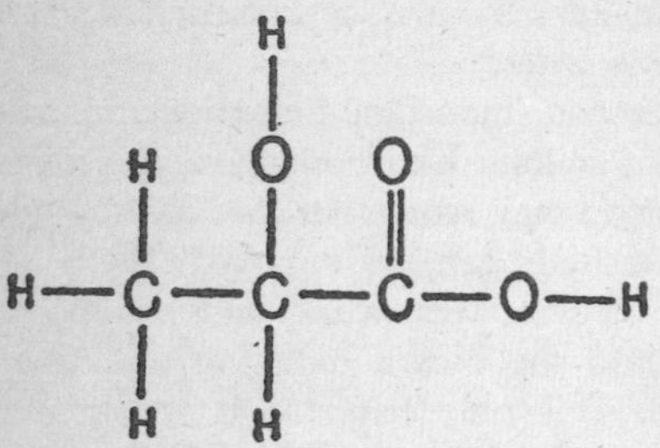

Figure 42—Lactic Acid

Lactic acid is what gives the sour taste to sour milk. (However, lactic acid is odorless. What causes the odor of sour milk is the butyric acid formed by the hydrolysis of some of the fat molecules in milk during souring.) Sometimes, instead of using baking powder in baking, the housewife can add sodium bicarbonate (baking soda) to the batter and then add some sour milk. The lactic acid will serve to produce carbonic acid and then, during the heating process, carbon dioxide.

Milk and cheese are the main source of calcium ion in the diet. That is why milk is so important for youngsters whose bones are growing and hardening (calcium ion being the most important component of bones). Nor can adults do without calcium ion, since some is always being lost to the body through the urine and must be replaced. Sometimes calcium deficiencies do exist in the human body and if there

---

fumaric acid. It is the set of reactions included in this cycle, which converts acetic acid (the most important intermediate) to carbon dioxide and water.

is any reason why milk can't be added to the diet, use is made of another hydroxy-acid.

This is *gluconic acid*. This has a molecule like glucose (hence its name) except that in place of the aldehyde group there is a carboxyl group. Gluconic acid can be combined with calcium ion to form *calcium gluconate*. Pills of calcium gluconate can then be used to supply the body with calcium.

Iron combined with gluconic acid in the form of *ferrous[2] gluconate* can be used in cases of iron deficiencies.

An example of an acid containing an ether group is *2:4-dichlorophenoxy acid*, usually abbreviated *2:4-D*. The compound has become famous in recent years as a weed-killer.

A compound something like lactic acid is *pyruvic acid*. This also has three carbon atoms. The middle carbon atom, however, instead of having a hydroxyl group attached, as in lactic acid, is part of a carbonyl group, like this:

Figure 43—Pyruvic Acid

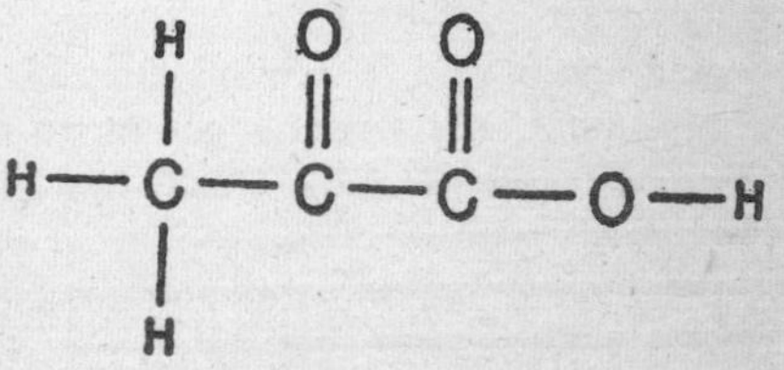

Pyruvic acid is a ketone, as well as a carboxylic acid. It is therefore an example of a *keto-acid*.

Next to acetic acid, pyruvic acid is probably the most important intermediate in the body. When a glucose molecule is broken up for energy, one of the many compounds it is changed into during the process is pyruvic acid. Once formed, pyruvic acid can change further in two different ways. If there is plenty of oxygen in the neighborhood, pyruvic acid loses a carbon atom and an oxygen atom. These combine with an atom of the oxygen I just mentioned as being available and form carbon dioxide. What is left of the pyruvic acid is

---

[2] The iron atom can form two kinds of ions, which are called *ferrous ion* and *ferric ion*. The "ferr" prefix comes from the Latin word for "iron."

acetic acid. The acetic acid can then be broken up further to carbon dioxide and water.

But what if there is not a sufficient supply of oxygen in the neighborhood of the pyruvic acid? This is exactly what happens in your muscles when you are working hard. Suppose you are chopping wood furiously or running a race. Your muscles are breaking up sugar molecules at a great rate. A quantity of pyruvic acid is being formed. The blood simply cannot get oxygen to the muscles fast enough to handle all that pyruvic acid. In that case the pyruvic acid simply adds two hydrogen atoms to its molecule and become lactic acid.

When the muscles change glucose to lactic acid, they get a certain amount of energy out of the deal.[3] The energy is only about 7 percent of the amount the body could get if it broke glucose down all the way to carbon dioxide and water. However, the 7 percent is enough for the muscles to get along on temporarily. In any case, it's the best the muscles can do without air.

But lactic acid is a blind alley. It just accumulates. As it accumulates, the muscles get more and more tired. Finally, they can work no more. They are holding all the lactic acid they can.

Once work is done, and the muscles are resting, they must collect oxygen with which to get rid of the lactic acid by changing it back to pyruvic acid. (The oxygen is needed to combine with the two extra hydrogen atoms in lactic acid, converting them to water.) It is because of this oxygen need that you continue panting for a period of time after you have stopped running or chopping wood. You have what is called an *oxygen debt* that must be paid off.

Castor Oil and Jelly

A long-chain hydoxy-acid, *ricinoleic acid,* was once a source of unpleasantness for a great many children. Ricinoleic acid is like oleic acid in its molecular structure. It also has a chain of eighteen carbon atoms with a carboxyl group at the end

---

[3] This process is known as *anaerobic glycolysis,* by the way, from Greek words meaning "sugar break-up without air."

and a double bond somewhere near the middle (though not exactly in the middle as in oleic acid). In addition, however, the ricinoleic acid molecule has one hydroxyl group attached to a carbon atom which is eleven atoms removed from the carboxyl group.

This added hydroxyl group has electrical properties that cause the whole molecule to cling to metal surfaces, lying flat as it does so. If a number of such molecules do so, they behave as a cushion between that metal surface and any other that may be pressing against it. The two surfaces slide against the yielding ricinoleic acid molecules instead of against each other. The ricinoleic acid acts as a *lubricant*, in other words.

The one fatty substance with molecules composed mainly of portions of ricinoleic acid molecule is the oil of the castor bean, commonly known as *castor oil*. Castor oil can be used to lubricate airplane motors. (Actually, ricinoleic acid itself would be unsatisfactory for the job because it would corrode the metal, but castor oil is non-corrosive). Castor oil can also be used to lubricate the human large intestine in cases of constipation. The inner walls of the intestine become slick and it can be emptied that much more easily. Any substance which encourages the emptying of the intestine is called a *laxative*.

This is where the sufferings of youth come in. An old-fashioned remedy for abdominal pains was a good dose of castor oil to "clean out the system." The trouble is that castor oil tastes quite horrible as I can testify from personal memory. Even when it is mixed with orange juice it is no pleasure.

There are dangers involved in taking excessive quantities of laxatives. If you make a habit of it, you may get to depend on them so much that you will find it difficult to get along without them. In the case of oily laxatives, vitamin trouble may also result. Vitamin A and vitamin D, as well as some others, are soluble in oils. If you coat the intestine with oil, these vitamins (sometimes referred to as the *fat-soluble vitamins*) stay in the oily coat and never get through the intestinal wall into the body. After a period of taking such laxatives, it would then be possible to become deficient in those vitamins even though there is plenty of each in the diet.

This can be prevented, to some extent, if the laxative is taken at bedtime, not just before or after a meal.

A sugar molecule may have the carbon at the end away from the aldehyde group become part of a carboxyl group. Such a molecule would have an aldehyde group at one end, a carboxyl group at the other, and hydroxyl groups attached to the carbon atoms in between. This is a *sugar acid,* or, as it is sometimes called, a *uronic acid.* If the hydroxyl groups have the same arrangement as in glucose, the particular sugar acid is *glucuronic acid.*

One of the uses the body finds for glucuronic acid is as a kind of rubbish bag. Suppose the body contains a compound it doesn't want. The compound may have been accidentally swallowed and absorbed, or taken in as a medicine. It may even be something the body once had a use for, but needs no longer. In any case, it is necessary for the body to get rid of it. What the body does most often is to combine this compound with glucuronic acid to form a *glucuronide.* Glucuronides are quite soluble and are easily eliminated by way of the urine. (That's where the "uron" part of the name comes from, by the way.)

If the uronic acid had the hydroxyl group arrangement of galactose, the result would be *galacturonic acid.* Galacturonic acid molecules can hook themselves into long chains just as ordinary sugars can. The resulting large molecule is called a *pectin.* Pectins occur in many fruits and vegetables. They dissolve in water to form *gels* (these are thick solutions that behave as though they were very soft solids). It is the pectins in fruit jellies, jams, and marmalades that give them their thickness. Pectin can also be used to thicken mayonnaise, malted milk drinks, and a number of other things.

Compounds that Clean

When a fatty acid, such as stearic acid, has lost a hydrogen ion, what remains behind is *stearate ion.* Stearate ion (or other similar fatty acid ions) has useful properties, but the question is, how does one go about getting it. Fatty acids are weak acids. When mixed with water, only 4 percent or so of the molecules lose hydrogen ions.

One way to encourage stearic acid molecules to lose hydrogen ions is to add some substance to the water which will attract the hydrogen ion and pull it away from the stearic acid molecule. A substance which will attract a hydrogen ion is called a *base*. (A base is the opposite of an acid. The molecules of an acid turn hydrogen ions loose. The molecules of a base snap hydrogen ions up.)

The strongest common base is *hydroxyl ion*.[4] Hydroxyl ion does not occur by itself, but makes up a part of compounds with molecules that also include other ions. It occurs, for instance, in *sodium hydroxide* (also called *lye* or *caustic soda*) and in *potassium hydroxide* (also called *caustic potash*).

If stearic acid is added to water which contains a bit of sodium hydroxide, the hydroxyl ion snatches at all the hydrogen ions it can. (A hydroxyl ion and a hydrogen ion combine to form a molecule of water.) The result is that just about all the stearic acid molecules lose hydrogen ions and become stearate ions.

Now fats and oils contain stearic acid groups (and other similar groups) as part of their molecules. If such fats and oils are heated with water containing a bit of sodium hydroxide, the molecules will hydrolyze into smaller fragments. Ordinarily, you might expect stearic acid to be formed. However, sodium hydroxide is present, so it is stearate ion that forms instead.

The stearate ion has a kind of split personality. The carboxylate group (which is the name given to a carboxyl group with a hydrogen ion lost) is very soluble in water. If the carbon chain to which the carboxyl group was attached was seven carbons in length or less, the entire molecule would be pulled into solution by the carboxylate group.

Stearate ion, however, has a 17-carbon chain attached to the carboxylate group. The carbon chain is not water-soluble and it's too long to be dragged in by one carboxylate group. The insoluble carbon chain is the other half of the split personality of the stearate ion.

---

[4] Hydroxyl ion is made up of an oxygen and a hydrogen atom but it is not the same as the hydroxyl group in an alcohol molecule. The hydroxyl ion has one excess electron and that gives it completely different properties.

The stearate ion tries to satisfy both halves of itself. The carboxylate group sticks into the water and the carbon chain sticks up out of the water. In order for this to happen, the stearate ion must stay in the surface film of the water. If more stearate ions are added to the water, they also crowd into the surface film and, eventually, fill it up. Substances which concentrate in a surface film, in this way, are called *surface-active compounds*.

The stearate ion (and other fatty acid ions like it) are associated with sodium ion, if sodium hydroxide were the base originally used to break up the fat molecule. A fatty acid ion in combination with sodium ion (or with any metal ion, for that mater) is called a *soap*. The process of breaking up fats and oils with sodium hydroxide is called *saponification* from the Latin word for "soap."

The value of soap depends on what it does to the surface film of water. When water (or any liquid) is quiet, the surface film is smooth and flat. But suppose a bottle half full of pure water is shaken up. It will froth and form bubbles. The bubbles will soon break, however, and the film will settle down and present a smooth, even surface once more, because it takes energy to keep a surface film in existence. Bubbles and unevenness increase the area of the film so that the energy required to maintain it in the bubbly uneven position is greater. The film just naturally returns to its minimum area, which requires least energy. The minimum area is that of an even, flat film.

What happens if you add a little soap to water and then shake it up? As soon as bubbles are formed, the water film forming that bubble will be filled with surface-active soap molecules. Such a soap-filled film takes less energy to maintain than does a film of water only. Furthermore, to cut down the film would mean kicking out the soap molecules, which is hard to do. For that reason, soap solutions will develop a layer of soapy bubbles at the surface, called *suds*. (Children take advantage of this when they use soapy water in bubble pipes.)

The main use of soap, however, is not to form soap bubbles but to clean hands, dishes, and clothing. Warm, running water will remove some foreign matter from such objects, but not all. The main trouble comes with dirt that happens to be oily.

Most dirt is exactly that. The skin is naturally oily, food particles on plates are usually fatty, and the soot that gets into our clothes is generally pretty greasy. Water can't dissolve these things; it can't even wet them. Naturally, it can't wash them away.

Water with a bit of soap in it is a different matter altogether. The soap molecules line up in the boundary between the water and the greasy particle. The carboxylate group of the stearate ion (or other similar ion) remains in the water but the carbon chain sticks into the grease. (The grease suits the carbon chain even better than the air does.)

Each grease particle is coated with soap molecules, all with the carboxylate groups pointing outward. The water can wet the carboxyl-coated grease particle easily now. The water lifts it up and floats it away; after all, carboxyl groups are very soluble in water.

Soap acts as a *detergent* (from a Latin word meaning "to wipe off"). Any substance with a molecule one end of which is soluble in water and the other end soluble in fat or hydrocarbon is a detergent.

The ordinary bar soap which we use in washing has, as I said, molecules made up of fatty acid ions and sodium ions. If, instead of sodium ion, potassium ions are present, the soap is much softer and is the kind used in shaving creams, for instance.

Fatty acid ions in combination with most other ions form soaps that are insoluble in water and useless for washing or cleaning. Water which contains these offending ions (usually ions of calcium, magnesium, or iron) forms weak suds or none at all when soap is added. Such water is called *hard water*.

Water, without the wrong type of ions, suds easily and this is *soft water*. Rain water and mountain spring water are soft while lake and river water are generally hard. Sea water is extremely hard.

In order to soften hard water, the undesirable ions must be removed. Sometimes, this can be done simply by boiling the water; at other times special compounds such as ammonia, sodium carbonate ("washing soda") or borax must be added.[5]

The body has its own detergents, named *bile acids*. These are steroids with one to three hydroxyl groups attached to the ring plus a carboxyl group at the end of one of the side-chains. The hydroxyl groups and carboxyl group are soluble in water; the rest of the molecule is soluble in fat. The detergent action is strengthened when bile acids are combined with certain other molecules to form *bile salts*.

The bile acids and bile salts are useful when it comes to the digestion of fats. The body's digestive fluids are watery in nature. They can digest carbohydrates easily because carbohydrates will either dissolve in the water or, at least, be wet by it. The fat, however, won't mix with the digestive fluids at all. They remain separate and standoffish in large, oily drops. Now the bile salts get into the film between the water and the fat and stay there. The general motion of the intestines breaks the fat globules into smaller drops. Ordinarily, the small drops would join up again, but the bile salts get into the new films as they are formed. This keeps the smaller drops from recombining.

This process continues and the fat globules get smaller and smaller until they are spread evenly through the digestive fluid. The smaller the globules, the more easily the fat can be digested.

When fat is divided up into smaller drops that spread evenly through water and don't settle out, the process is called *emulsification* or *homogenization*. We're all familiar with homogenized milk, for instance, in which the cream has been split up into tiny drops and won't separate and rise to the top. The tiny drops, once formed, remain apart because of the presence of natural surface-active compounds in the milk.

[5] Most of us have had experience with rings of "dirt" left behind in the bathtub after a bath. This usually isn't just grime from the person who has been bathing. It is most likely to consist of a gummy, insoluble deposit of fatty acid ions combined with the calcium or magnesium ions in the bath water. Practically nothing, however, is completely useless, even the stuff in bathtub rings. Such insoluble soaps are used in lubricating greases.

Chapter 11

Combinations Cancel Out

Nail-Polish Remover and Headache Pills

THE CARBOXYL group of one compound and the hydroxyl group of another can condense, like this:

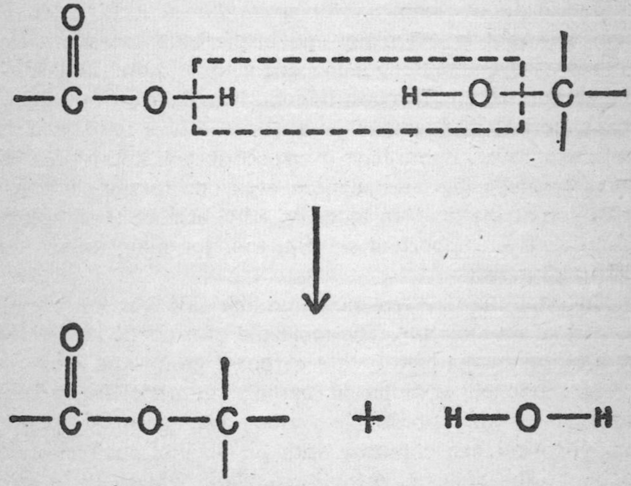

Figure 44—Esterification (active groups only)

A compound that contains the atom combination that results is called an *ester* and the process of forming an ester is called *esterification*. By combining in this way, both acid and alcohol lose part of the group that gives each its properties. The ester is neither an acid nor an alcohol, therefore. The combination has cancelled out the properties of each.[1]

---

[1] Those of you who do crossword puzzles may recognize the word "ester" as something which is usually defined in the puzzle as a "compound ether." This dates back to the primitive days of chemistry and no modern chemist would ever dream of defining

Many of the simpler esters are pleasant substances with fruity odors. (The odors are liable to become rather overpowering if present in too great concentration, however.) A typical ester is *isoamyl acetate*.[2] This has a strong odor of bananas. Other similar esters smell of pears, peaches, apples, pineapples, strawberries, apricots, and so on. The odor of these fruits and at least part of their flavor is due to the esters. The odors of flowers are also caused, sometimes, by the presence of esters. Perfumers can add the odors of jasmine, gardenia, or geranium to their products by use of the proper ester.

One of the best-known esters is *ethyl acetate*. It has an odor like pears but is less fruity and just a little too sharp to be entirely pleasant. Young ladies ought to be quite familiar with the compound and its odor, though. Ethyl acetate will dissolve the materials in fingernail polish and so it is used as a nail-polish remover. If you have ever used it, you know what ethyl acetate smells like and so does everyone in the same room with you at the time. In industry, ethyl acetate (boiling point, 77° C.) is an important solvent, too, for many things other than nail-polish.

An ester that is even more familiar involves *salicylic acid* as part of its molecule. The molecule of salicylic acid consists of a benzene ring with both a carboxyl group and a hydroxyl group attached at adjacent carbon atoms. This gives the molecule a kind of double action. The carboxyl group of salicylic acid can condense with an alcohol such as methyl alcohol. The result is *methyl salicylate*, which has a strong and pleasant wintergreen odor.[8]

---

an ester so. Crossword puzzle makers just copy that definition from one another and will probably still be calling esters compound ethers a hundred years from now.

[2] An ester is named from the acid and alcohol that condense to form it. For instance isoamyl acetate is formed by condensing isoamyl alcohol (a five-carbon alcohol with a branched chain) with acetic acid. The alcohol is usually named first. The "ate" suffix on the acid part of the name is usual whenever the hydrogen ion of the acid is replaced by something else.

[8] Methyl salicylate is sometimes called *oil of wintergreen*, and is an example of an *essential oil*. The word "essential," as used here, does not mean that it is particularly "necessary." It means that it

The hydroxyl group in salicylic acid can condense, on the other hand, with a carboxylic acid, such as acetic acid. The result is *acetylsalicylic acid* and that is the familiar ester I referred to in the previous paragraph. You have certainly seen this ester and the chances are that you have swallowed considerable quantities of it. You won't find this hard to believe once I tell you that the common name of acetylsalicylic acid is *aspirin*.

Salicylic acid and compounds related to it relieve pain and lower fever. (That is, they are *analgesics* and *anti-pyretics*.) Methyl salicylate is used externally to rub on the skin over aching muscles. Aspirin is taken internally as you all know. Aspirin is probably the most frequently taken of all medicines. Hundreds of millions of tablets have been manufactured since 1899 when it was first used as a medicine. Even those headache tablets that are not called aspirin usually have aspirin as one of the ingredients.

Esters made up through the combination of long-chain alcohols with long-chain acids are solids at room temperature. There are so many carbon and hydrogen atoms in such molecules and so few oxygen atoms that these esters behave like solid hydrocarbons in many ways. Such an ester, with long carbon chains on either side of the ester group is a *wax*. (Remember that a mixture of solid hydrocarbons is known as paraffin wax, because of the similarity in properties, even though paraffin is not a true wax.) A familiar example is *beeswax*[4] which bees manufacture and out of which they build their honeycombs. Another is *shellac,* which is produced by the lac insect of India.

Man secretes a waxy material, also, by means of *little sebaceous glands* that are found near the roots of each hair. The material they manufacture is called *sebum*. This coats the hair as it grows and spreads out over the skin, too, as a protective layer. Much of the sebum is made up of esters of

---

is derived from an "essence," that is, a fragrant plant constituent. Other essential oils are condensations of the alcohol, menthol with acetic acid or benzoic acid. Such combinations are responsible for the odor and taste of peppermint and cloves, respectively.

[4] The word "wax" comes from an old Anglo-Saxon word for "beeswax."

cholesterol with various fatty acids. Such *cholesteryl esters* or *cholesterides* are waxy in character. (Earwax, in fact, is mostly an accumulation of sebum.)

It is quite common these days for hair and skin lotions to contain *lanolin*. This is sheep sebum (with their woolly coats, sheep secrete a great deal of sebum) and is therefore sometimes called *wool wax*. This is intended to replace the protective sebum that has been washed out of human hair and skin by the frequent use of soap.

Another animal wax of considerable usefulness is *spermaceti*, which is obtained from the head of the sperm whale. It, like beeswax, is used in making candles. It is also used in ointment. Spermaceti contains esters of a long chain alcohol (16 carbon atoms) called *cetyl alcohol*. (The stem "cet" comes from the Latin word for "whale.") Cetyl alcohol, obtained from spermaceti, is used in shampoos, lipstick, and other cosmetics.

Plants also produce waxes. These are used by the plant mostly as a coating for leaves, keeping them waterproof. Palm leaves are good sources and *carnauba wax* comes from the leaves of the carnauba palm of Brazil. Carnauba wax is used in such things as shoe polish and floor wax.

The First Vitamin

Sometimes when a carboxyl group and a hydroxyl group occur in the same molecule, the two groups can condense with one another. An *internal ester* is formed as one part of the molecule condenses with another part. An internal ester is often called a *lactone*.[5]

Glucuronic acid and other sugar acids form lactones very easily. The most important example for the human being

[5] The word "lactone" comes from lactic acid which has a molecule that contains both a carboxyl group and a hydroxyl group. Nevertheless, lactic acid does not form lactones because the two groups are too close together to condense. (You can imagine, as a comparison, a situation where you are crowded too closely in a subway train to be able to shake hands with the man you are crowded against.) Two molecules of lactic acid can condense to form a kind of molecule known as a *lactide*, but we won't have to be concerned with that in this book.

involves an acid known as *3-ketogulonic acid*. It is a six-carbon compound which is like gluconic acid (which I mentioned in the previous chapter) except that its hydroxyl groups are arranged differently and that it has a double bond in the middle of the chain. This compound forms a lactone which is known as *ascorbic acid* and thereby hangs a tale.

When men first began to make long sea-voyages it was noticed that after a long time at sea, sailors were likely to suffer from a disease known as *scurvy*. People with scurvy bruise and bleed easily, especially about the gums. Their joints become painful and wounds heal very slowly. The sailor becomes unfit for work and, if the disease gets bad enough, he dies.

For many centuries, the cause of scurvy was unknown, but today we know that the trouble lay in the sailors' diet. The problem of food on ships was a difficult one in the days before refrigeration. Only food which would not spoil, such as dried biscuit ("hardtack") or salt pork, could be carried on long voyages.

Foods such as these might grow tiresome after a while, but they supplied the sailor with all he needed for energy and for most other purposes. However, human beings need small quantities of certain chemicals in their diet if their bodies are to work well. Salt pork, hardtack, and other such foods lack one such chemical in particular. From lack of that one substance, scurvy developed.

About two hundred years ago, the British Navy started to make its sailors drink a regular ration of lime juice. The sailors probably resented having to do it, being much fonder of "grog" (an alcoholic drink), I imagine, but the lime juice prevented scurvy. Nobody knew why at the time, but it did. (It was for that reason, by the way, that British sailors first got their nickname of "limey" and that a section of the London dock area came to be known as "Limehouse.")

Then about 1900, nutrition experts started finding out about vitamins and, sure enough, they discovered the chemical which prevented scurvy when present in the diet. That chemical was first isolated in 1928 and it turned out to be ascorbic acid. (The word "ascorbic" means "no scurvy" since the Latin word for scurvy is "scorbutus.")

So it turns out that scurvy was the first vitamin-deficiency disease that was deliberately treated by adjusting the diet. Ascorbic acid was the first vitamin to be used to cure a disease (even if at the time the British admirals didn't realize what they were really doing).

Ascorbic acid, often called *vitamin C*,[6] is found in milk, and in fresh fruits and vegetables. The citrus fruits (including limes, of course) are quite rich in it. Orange juice is one of the first items of food added to an infant's milk diet because of the vitamin C that the juice contains.

Ascorbic acid is the most fragile of the vitamins. Heat destroys it rather quickly so that not much of it survives in foods that have been thoroughly cooked. Moreover, it is soluble in water. (Of the vitamins I have mentioned, ascorbic acid is the first to belong to the class of the *water-soluble vitamins*.) If vegetables are cooked in a quantity of water, the vitamin will end in the water and not in the vegetable. (And usually the water is thrown out.)

Most animals, by the way, can make their own ascorbic acid and don't have to have it in their diet. Cattle, for instance, make their own. They can't possibly have scurvy. Included among the few animals that have lost the ability to make ascorbic acid are the guinea-pig and the primates. The primates are a group of animals that include apes and monkeys, and, of course, man.

The Tell-Tale Color

An interesting but rather complicated lactone (with three separate benzene rings in its molecule) is *phenolphthalein*. Phenolphthalein is a white solid which will dissolve in ethyl

[6] The American Medical Association disapproves of the name "ascorbic acid" because it mentions the disease against which the chemical can be used. They don't like to see anything encourage a patient to think he knows which drug is good for what disease and start dosing himself accordingly. (I think they are right in this. Self-dosing can be very harmful.) The A.M.A. therefore tried to introduce the name *cevitamic acid* for ascorbic acid, taking this name from vitamin C. However, the A.M.A. name seems never to have caught on.

alcohol to form a colorless solution. If a bit of the dissolved phenolphthalein is added to water, nothing happens. The water remains colorless.

But now suppose a solution of a basic substance such as sodium hydroxide, also colorless, is added to the water containing the phenolphthalein. Under the influence of the base, the lactone portion of the phenolphthalein molecule breaks apart. Other minor changes also take place. The changed molecule is now a deep red in color.

Thus, a drop of a colorless liquid added to a glassful of a colorless liquid results in a glassful of a deeply colored liquid. Stage magicians use tricks of this sort to change water into "wine."

If you now add a bit of acid to the red solution, the phenolphthalein molecules join up in the original lactone form and are colorless once more. The "wine" is reconverted to water.

This sort of thing is very useful to chemists. Suppose a chemist has a solution which contains a certain amount of acid and he wants to know exactly how much that "certain amount" is. He adds a bit of phenolphthalein and then starts adding a solution of base, drop by drop. He has prepared the base carefully so that he knows exactly how much sodium hydroxide (or any other base he's using) is contained in any given quantity of the solution.[7]

At first the added base combines with the acid in the solution as fast as it is added and nothing happens. Finally, though, all the acid is used up. The next drop of base which is added has no acid to combine with. It is free to act on the phenolphthalein and the whole solution suddenly turns red.

The chemist knows how much base he has added up to that point[8] and so he can calculate the amount of acid he

[7] A solution of any substance prepared in such a way that you know exactly how much of the substance present in a given quantity of the solution is a *standard solution*.

[8] He uses a long tube, with markings on the side to show how much solution he has let out of the lower end. (There is a stopcock at the lower end which can slow down the flow or stop it altogether.) Such a tube is called a *burette* and the process of adding one chemical to another until some *endpoint* (like a color change) is reached is known as a *titration*.

had, for he knows how many molecules of a particular acid combine with each molecule of a particular base. It is the sudden color change in phenolphthalein that indicates the answer and phenolphthalein is therefore an example of a type of compound called an *indicator*.

There are many other compounds which change color as certain chemical conditions (usually the acidity) change. Any of these can be used to give information to the chemist. Some of the most important methods of chemical analysis depend on such color changes.

Instruments have been designed that can measure the amount of color present in solutions much more sensitively and accurately than the human eye can. Colors in the ultra-violet and the infra-red which the human eye can't see are detected by instruments and can be made to give useful information.

Phenolphthalein, by the way, irritates the walls of the intestine into activity when it is taken internally. It can, in this way, relieve constipation. Some of our most common chocolate or gum laxatives contain phenolphthalein as the active ingredient. (The chocolate or gum is just there to make it pleasant to take.)

Substitutes for Silk and Glass

A molecule containing more than one hydroxyl group (or more than one carboxyl group) can form esters at more than one place, naturally.

Consider cellulose, for instance. Its molecule is made up of long strings of glucose residues. Each glucose molecule has five hydroxyl groups to begin with, but two are used up in forming links with other glucose molecules in order that cellulose might result. That still leaves three hydroxyl groups available for condensation on each glucose residue. Acetic acid can be condensed on to some or all of these to form *cellulose acetate*.

Cellulose acetate (usually the kind with two acetate groups for each glucose residue) can be dissolved in acetone and forced through very fine holes. A thin stream of the liquid squirts out of each hole. As the acetone evaporates, it leaves behind an even thinner fiber of cellulose acetate. This is another variety of rayon (already mentioned in Chapter 8) an early silk substitute. This variety is *acetate rayon*, or *Celanese*.

Cellulose acetate can also be forced through a slot so as to form a flexible film. It is such film that is used in movie cameras.

You don't need to start with a large molecule to end with one, of course. Suppose you begin with *phthallic acid* (which has a molecule made up of a benzene ring to which two carboxyl groups are attached at adjacent points in the ring) and glycerol which, you may remember, has three hydroxyl groups per molecule. These two compounds can condense, one hydroxyl group to one carboxyl group, and each will have groups left over with which to condense with still other molecules. Long chains are formed and the end result is a semi-solid material called an *alkyd resin*.

The alkyd resins are added to paints, enamels, lacquers, and varnishes of various kinds. They remain behind in the final film, which they make tougher and more flexible. In this way they keep a painted surface in better condition for a longer time.

A useful plastic is formed out of a simple ester called *methyl methacrylate*. This ester contains four carbon atoms and one double bond. It is the double bond that enables neighboring molecules to polymerize and form long chains, just as in the case of ethylene. The final result is *Plexiglas* or *Lucite*. (In England it is called *Perspex*.) This is a transparent substance that can be molded into all sorts of shapes. It is glass-like in appearance and is, in fact, sometimes spoken of as "organic glass." It is lighter than ordinary glass and will not shatter. It is also softer than ordinary glass, however, and far more easily scratched. In addition, it can be attacked by organic liquids by which glass is unaffected.

Another polymer containing a series of ester links is *Dacron*. This can be formed into strong fibers and is one of the synthetic fibers out of which garments are made these days. Dacron cloth is more crease-resistant than is cloth made out of natural fibers. In England this polymer is called *Terylene*.

Fats, at Last

When I first started talking about carboxylic acids, I said they were sometimes called fatty acids because they formed part of the molecules of fats. Now I am finally ready to talk about fats.

In the first place, we all know by experience what a fat is. It is a substance of plant or animal origin that won't dissolve in water, that has a greasy feel, and that will leave a grease spot on paper. If solid, it is called a *fat*, but if liquid it is generally called an *oil*.[9]

The molecules of fats and oil are esters of glycerol and are called *glycerides*. Each of the three hydroxyl groups in a glycerol molecule is condensed with the carboxyl group of a fatty acid to form a molecule of a fat or oil. The fatty acids involved can have as few as four carbon atoms in their chain or as many as twenty-four. They can be completely saturated or can have anywhere from one to five double bonds. Naturally, every molecule with a particular assortment of fatty acids is different from every molecule with a slightly different assortment. Natural fats and oils are complicated mixtures of different glycerides.

Mixtures of glycerides which contain mostly saturated fatty acids as part of their molecules are solid. The fat of warm-blooded animals—suet, tallow, lard, chicken-fat—falls into this classification. Mixtures of glycerides containing sizeable quantities of unsaturated fatty acids as part of their molecules are liquid. The fat of cold-blooded animals and of plants come under this heading—cod-liver oil, cottonseed oil, and so on. (Some plant fats are solid. Examples are those from some kinds of palm trees.)

Oleic acid occurs in all natural fats and oils. Olive oil, in particular, has three times as much oleic acid forming part of its molecules, as it does all other fatty acids combined. Olive oil was the most important oil of ancient Greece and Rome (and of the Mediterranean countries even today). The very

---

[9] Sometimes liquid fats are called *fatty oils* to distinguish them from "oils" with different types of molecules such as mineral oils, essential oils, and so on.

words "oil" and "oleic" come from the Greek and Latin words for "olive."

In animals, fats are the chief substances used for the storing of energy. A fat molecule will hold over twice as much energy as a glycogen molecule of the same size. The hydrogen atoms of a fat molecule are all attached to carbon atoms. Breaking the carbon-hydrogen bond and attaching the hydrogen atoms to oxygen is the chemical process that produces energy in the body. In glycogen, nearly half the hydrogen atoms are already attached to oxygen atoms and no energy can be extracted from those bonds. (On the other hand, glycogen is more easily handled by the body than fat is so each type of molecule has its advantages.)

The color of pure fat is white and pure oil is colorless. Yellow, orange, or red color is due to the presence of small quantities of carotene and similar compounds. Olive oil sometimes has a greenish cast because it contains a bit of chlorophyll, the green coloring matter in leaves.

Fats in the Kitchen

The housewife uses fat for preparing food. Fats (or oils) can be heated to much higher temperature than water can. They can be heated to 200° C. or even 300° C. before they start smoking. Water boils at 100° C. and cannot be heated to higher temperatures except in a pressure cooker.

When food is fried in fat, the extra heat sears the outside and allows the inner portion to retain its juices. The fat also gives an additional flavor to the food and adds calories for those who need them.

Natural fats often used for cooking are butter (which is fat obtained from milk) and lard among the animal fats; olive oil and peanut oil among the plant oils.

In general, such fats are considerably more expensive than some vegetable oils that can't be used for cooking. For instance, the seeds of the cotton plant are about 25 percent oil. Considering all the cotton that is produced in the country, you can see how common cotton-seed oil must be. Yet it can't be used for cooking because it has an unpleasant flavor.

This flavor is due to the unsaturated fatty acids that occur as part of its molecules. If cotton-seed oil is treated with hydrogen gas under the proper conditions, the hydrogen atoms add on to the double bond. All the fatty acid chains become saturated. This results in the oil being changed to a solid fat that is quite suitable for cooking.

Such hydrogenated oils are the *vegetable shortenings* that are quite common in the kitchen these days.

Vegetable oils can also be hydrogenated to a smaller extent so that they have the same consistency as butter. Such a fat is called *margarine*.

Fats sometimes spoil or grow rancid when allowed to stand too long, particularly without refrigeration. This can happen in one of two ways. First, small quantities of the glycerides may hydrolyze and the fatty acids will break loose from the ester molecule. Ordinarily, this wouldn't matter much because it only happens to a small extent and you would never tell the difference. However, if the fatty acid that breaks loose is a short-chain one (ten carbon atoms or less), it is foul-smelling. Even tiny quantities of such a fatty acid in food would make it uneatable.

The only common fat that contains these small-chain fatty acids is butter. Butter (and milk, which contains butter-fat) must be kept refrigerated to prevent rancidity.[10] (Margarine, on the other hand, contains no short-chain fatty acids as part of its molecules. For that reason, it needn't be kept refrigerated unless you just don't want it to get too soft.)

Another way in which fats or oils may go rancid is through the addition of oxygen atoms to any double bonds present in the molecules. A pair of oxygen atoms are added at a double bond and what is called a *fatty acid peroxide* is formed. These have an unpleasant taste.

Naturally, fats without double bonds can't go rancid in this way. For this reason, vegetable shortenings can be allowed to

[10] Milk can be allowed to go "sour" without going "rancid" if proper types of bacteria are added. Yogurt, acidophilus milk, and sour cream are all produced this way and are quite pleasant. Some cheeses are allowed to "ripen" and then may contain some short-chain fatty acids. These are pretty smelly, but connoisseurs who have become accustomed to them find them delicious.

stand at room temperature for long periods of time without spoiling.

Paint

Sometimes an oil may contain an unusual amount of linoleic acid and linolenic acid as part of its molecules. Oil molecules with all the double bonds those acids have, will add on oxygen atoms at those double bonds if exposed to air. The oxygen atoms are added on in pairs and these connect the hydrocarbon chains of neighboring molecules. In this way, the oil polymerizes in a way and becomes made up of giant interconnected molecules. It becomes a tough solid. It seems to dry up, in other words, and such oils are called *drying oils*.

The most common drying oil is *linseed oil,* which comes from the seed of the flax plant.[11] If a drying oil is spread over a wood or metal, it forms a tough film as it sets. This film is air-proof and waterproof. By keeping air and water away from the surface underneath, it prevents wood from warping or rotting and keeps metal from rusting or corroding. It is a protective cover.

Pigments of various colors (usually inorganic compounds made up of molecules containing atoms such as those of lead, zinc, titanium, or chromium) are added to make *paint*. If resins are added to make the film tougher and less brittle, the result is a *varnish*. (All sorts of synthetic resins and polymers are added to paints these days.)

Linseed oil can be used for other things as well as paint. If it is coated on canvas, the result is *oilcloth*. If it is mixed with resins and cork particles are added, the result is *linoleum*.

---

[11] "Lin" is an old word for "flax." The word "linen" for flax fiber comes from that. So do the words "linseed," "linoleic," and "linolenic."

Epilogue—*What Is Yet to Be Told*

The final paragraphs of the last chapter may seem like an abrupt end to my discussion of The World of Carbon; and so they would be if it were really the end. But it is not.

So far, I have discussed only those organic compounds with molecules made up of atoms of carbon, hydrogen, the halogens, and oxygen. These have included a variety of substances, from gasoline to paint, and in discussing them all I have managed to fill this book and leave no room for more. I must stop here.

I have not yet discussed penicillin, aureomycin, or any of the other ' miracle drugs." I haven't discussed the B vitamins. I haven't mentioned explosives or told what it is that gives onions their taste and skunks their smell. I haven't described the compound that makes our blood red, or the one that makes grass green.

I haven't described the most important substances in living tissues: the proteins and nucleic acids, which supervise body chemistry, pass on characteristics from parents to children, and make all the difference between living tissue and dead matter.

There are enough things I haven't described—all of them organic compounds, all members of The World of Carbon—to fill another book, which is exactly what I have done.

This second book deals with those organic compounds which contain varieties of atoms that I have not dealt with so far in *The World of Carbon*. Most of these compounds (but not all) will contain one or more atoms of *nitrogen* in their molecules. Because of this, I have called the second book which deals with them *The World of Nitrogen*.

If you have found this book useful and interesting, I hope you will read the next one.

Index

Index